Grade 3

Home-School Connection

Macmillan
McGraw-Hill

The McGraw·Hill Companies

 **Macmillan McGraw-Hill**

Published by Macmillan/McGraw-Hill, of McGraw-Hill Education, a division of The McGraw-Hill Companies, Inc., Two Penn Plaza, New York, New York 10121-2298.

Printed in the United States of America

7 8 9 021 10 09 08

Dear Family Member:

You can help your child practice reading skills taught at school. Working together you and your child can become partners in learning.

Each week your child will bring home:

- A **letter** that tells you about the book the class is reading that week

- Three **homework activities** that will improve reading skills and offer practice with words your child is learning

- A **story** for the two of you to read together

Your interest, praise, and encouragement are sure to lead to your child's success.

Queridos familiares:

Con su ayuda, su niño/a puede practicar las destrezas de lectura aprendidas en la escuela. Este trabajo conjunto les permitirá ser compañeros de aprendizaje.

Cada semana, su niño/a va a llevar a casa lo siguiente:

- Una **carta** contándole acerca lo que ha leído en clase durante esa semana.

- Tres **actividades de tareas para el hogar** para mejorar las destrezas de lectura y practicar las palabras que está aprendiendo.

- También llevará a casa un **cuento** para que lo lean juntos.

Su interés, apoyo y estímulo guiarán a su niño/a al éxito.

Contents

Beginning of the Year Letter
in English and Spanish

● On-Level Books

● On-Level Books

Word Workout

WORDS TO KNOW

chuckled	downstairs	fumbled
nervous	nonsense	trudged

Crowded Sentences Let's see how many of the words we can use in one sentence. We can keep going until we're worn out!

SPELLING WORDS

sick	rock	luck	clap	step
mess	head	shut	crop	snack
jump	click	pond	miss	stamp

Name That Vowel I'll read a word from the list. Tell me the letter that makes the vowel sound and then spell the word. We can both think of other words with the same vowel sound before you spell the next word.

(fold here)

Home-School Connection

Dear Family Member:

This week, I'm reading *First Day Jitters*. The story is about Sarah, who doesn't want to get out of bed and go to her new school. In class, I've been learning about character, setting, and plot. I'm keeping track of who is in the story, where and when it takes place, and what happens. This story begins in Sarah's bedroom. I think another part of the story will be set in school.

This Week's Skills

Comprehension: character, setting, plot

Vocabulary: compound words

Spelling/Phonics: the short vowel letters **a, e, i, o, u**

Name _____

Story Board

Let's talk about the pictures and captions. We'll decide if they tell about a character, a setting, or an event in the plot. You can circle our decision.

Zorro was a happy dog. He thought he was the best ballplayer in the world.

Character   Setting   Plot

Zorro played "Fetch." First he ran. Then he jumped up into the air and caught the ball in his mouth.

Character   Setting   Plot

There were tennis balls all over the backyard.

Character   Setting   Plot

Zorro piled up the balls.

Character   Setting   Plot

He made a big sign.

Character   Setting   Plot

Zorro made lots of money. He kept the last ball for himself.

Character   Setting   Plot

Ejercicio de palabras

PALABRAS DE VOCABULARIO

chuckled	downstairs	fumbled
nervous	nonsense	trudged

Oraciones con muchas palabras Veamos cuántas palabras podemos usar en una oración. ¡Podemos seguir hasta que nos cansemos!

PALABRAS DE ORTOGRAFÍA

sick	rock	luck	clap	step
mess	head	shut	crop	snack
jump	click	pond	miss	stamp

Nombra esa vocal Voy a leer una palabra de la lista. Dime la letra que suena como la vocal y luego deletrea la palabra. Ambos podemos pensar en otras palabras que tengan el mismo sonido de la vocal antes de escribir la próxima palabra.

(fold here)

© Macmillan/McGraw-Hill

Conexión con el hogar

Queridos familiares:

Esta semana estoy leyendo *First Day Jitters*. El cuento es acerca de Sarah, que no quiere levantarse de la cama para ir a su escuela nueva. En clase, aprendí sobre los personajes, el ambiente y el argumento. Mantengo un registro de quién está en el cuento, en dónde y cuándo ocurre, y qué ocurre. Este cuento comienza en la habitación de Sarah. Pienso que la otra parte del cuento será en la escuela.

Destrezas de la semana

Comprensión: personajes, ambiente, argumento

Vocabulario: palabras compuestas

Ortografía/Fonética: las letras de vocales cortes **a, e, i, o, u**

Nombre _____

Mapa del cuento

Hablemos acerca de los dibujos y los textos. Decidiremos si hablan acerca de un personaje, un lugar o un suceso en el argumento. Puedes encerrar en un círculo nuestra decisión.

Zorro was a happy dog. He thought he was the best ball-player in the world.

Character   Setting   Plot

Zorro played "Fetch." First he ran. Then he jumped up into the air and caught the ball in his mouth.

Character   Setting   Plot

There were tennis balls all over the backyard.

Character   Setting   Plot

Zorro piled up the balls.

Character   Setting   Plot

He made a big sign.

Character   Setting   Plot

Zorro made lots of money. He kept the last ball for himself.

Character   Setting   Plot

Comprehension Check

Retell the Story

Use a Story Map to retell what happens in the story, where it takes place, and who the characters are.

Think and Compare

1. Reread page 10. What made Jay start thinking about his old school? How do his thoughts help you know more about his character? *(Analyze Character, Setting, and Plot)*

2. Think about being a stranger in a place where other people know each other well. How would you feel? What would make it easier for you? *(Apply)*

3. What are some reasons that kids might have to change from one school to another? *(Evaluate)*

16

The New Kid

by Lisa deMauro
illustrated by Dusan Petricic

Table of Contents

Chapter 1
The New School

One Monday in November, Jay and his mother drove to a yellow brick building with a sign in front that said: "Rosewood Middle School." It was a big building—much taller than Jay's old school.

Jay's mother filled out lots of forms. Before they left, the school principal, Ms. Tucker, came out of her office and shook Jay's hand. "Welcome to Rosewood," she said. "We'll see you tomorrow."

2

As Jay took a sip of juice, he realized something: For the first time that day, he was really enjoying himself. He felt relieved. It would take some getting used to, but maybe being the new kid wouldn't be so terrible after all.

The New Kid

15

Jay told Rachel and Tom about his morning in class. "You're lucky," said Tom. "I had Mr. Marcus last year and he's great."

Rachel agreed. "Sometimes you think he's talking nonsense, but he always makes sense in the end. And you learn a lot!"

14

© 2007 Macmillan/McGraw-Hill

On Tuesday morning, Jay's older sister, Eva, gave him a ride to school. "Are you nervous?" she asked. Jay shrugged and then nodded. "I hate being the new kid," he admitted.

Eva chuckled. "You'll feel better after you've gotten to know a few people. Trust me!"

Eva watched Jay join the crowd of students who were waiting to go into the building. Then she drove down the road toward the high school.

3

"Jay!" someone yelled. Jay spun around so fast that he bumped into another, bigger student, knocking him to the ground.

"Nice move," said the boy. He looked pretty annoyed as he got back on his feet.

4

Jay was embarrassed, but Tom started to laugh. "No big deal," he said, making a face at his sister.

As they moved through the line, Rachel and Tom gave Jay advice about the food. Then they took their trays to a table and sat down.

13

Jay felt like climbing into a hole. He looked down at his shoes so he wouldn't have to face them.

"Hey," said the girl. Jay looked up. She was smiling. "My name is Rachel," she said. "You're new, right?" Jay nodded.

"This is my brother, Tom," said Rachel. "Did you really knock him down? I wish I'd been there."

12

"Sorry," said Jay, but the boy had already turned his back. Jay looked around. Whoever had called his name must have been talking to someone else.

5

Chapter 2

More Trouble

In the hallway, Jay checked the paper he had gotten from the school office. It said: Room 314. He headed toward a stairwell and climbed three flights. But when he got upstairs, the first room he saw was 401.

On the lunch line, the girl and boy in front of Jay were talking. When the boy turned around, Jay saw that it was the kid he'd knocked down that morning.

The boy saw Jay and said something to the girl. She turned, and Jay knew her too! It was the girl he'd gotten tangled up with on the stairs.

6

11

Chapter 4
Making New Friends

When the lunch bell rang, the class headed for the door. Jay trudged along to the huge, crowded lunchroom. He thought about the sunny cafeteria in his old school where he always sat with his best friend, Ali. Today he'd be eating by himself.

10

Jay would have to go back downstairs. As he turned around, he ran into a crowd of students heading up the stairway.

One girl was right in his way. She stepped aside, but he stepped in the same direction. They went back and forth like this until the girl finally stood still. She pointed down the stairs, bowed, and said, "After you."

Jay blushed and ran down the stairs. "This is turning out to be a pretty bad day," he thought.

7

Chapter 3

Meeting Mr. Marcus

Now Jay was really late. Room 314 was locked so Jay knocked softly. A very tall man opened the door. He had a very serious expression on his face.

TODAY'S SCHEDULE
READING
MATH
SOCIAL STUDIES
LUNCH

The New Kid

"State your reason for interrupting my class," he said. Jay fumbled in his pocket for the paper.

"I'm in this class," he said in a quiet voice. Mr. Marcus pulled the paper from between Jay's fingers and studied it. Then he smiled.

"Why didn't you say so?" he asked. "Hurry, take a seat. Later we'll learn about your past, your present, and your hopes for the future. But now, there's work to do."

"What a weird teacher!" thought Jay, taking the nearest empty seat he could find. More than ever, he wished he were back in his old school.

Word Workout

WORDS TO KNOW

announced	crackle	envelope
photograph	soared	starry

Words Make the Story Let's look at the words together and make up a mystery story using all of them. We could start like this: The girl found an old photograph hidden in an envelope.

SPELLING WORDS

globe	life	home	safe	date
rice	plane	smile	lake	fine
grade	rose	come	smoke	wise

Speed Spell We're going to see how many words you can spell in two minutes. Do you want to see if you can top your first score? We can play Speed Spell again.

© Macmillan/McGraw-Hill

(fold here)

Home-School Connection

Dear Family Member:

The story we are reading in class this week is about a boy named Juno. He gets a letter from his grandmother in Korea. He cannot read what she has written because he does not know her language. The story is called *Dear Juno*. I'm learning about the different parts of a story—character, setting, and plot. I'm paying attention to these things as I am reading. I want to know Juno better and what he does to understand his grandmother's letter.

This Week's Skills

Comprehension: character, setting, plot

Vocabulary: sentence clues

Spelling/Phonics: words with long vowel sounds, such as *make, kite,* and *hope*

Name _____

Be an Author

Look at each picture and then we'll talk about how we could use it to create a character, a setting, and a plot. You can fill in our decisions on the notepad.

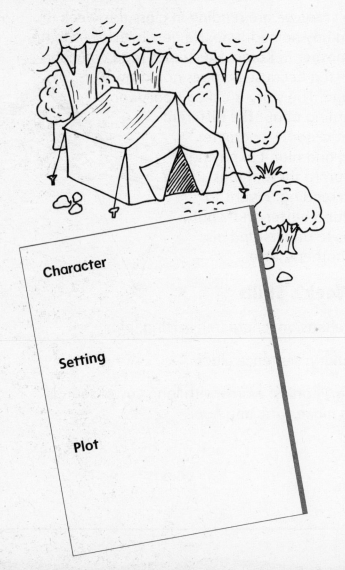

Character

Setting

Plot

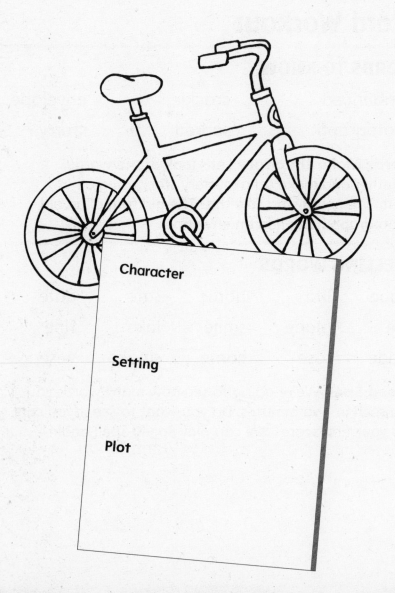

Character

Setting

Plot

Ejercicio de palabras

PALABRAS DE VOCABULARIO

announced	crackle	envelope
photograph	soared	starry

Las palabras hacen el relato Observemos juntos las palabras y escribamos un relato de misterio usando todas las palabras. Podríamos comenzar así: *The girl found an old photograph hidden in an envelope.*

PALABRAS DE ORTOGRAFÍA

globe	life	home	safe	date
rice	plane	smile	lake	fine
grade	rose	come	smoke	wise

Ortografía veloz Vamos a ver cuántas palabras puedes deletrear en dos minutos. ¿Quieres ver si puedes mejorar tu primer puntaje? Podemos jugar otra vez al juego de ortografía veloz.

© Macmillan/McGraw-Hill · (fold here)

Conexión con el hogar

Queridos familiares:

El relato que estamos leyendo en clase esta semana es acerca de un niño que se llama Juno. Él recibe una carta de su abuela que vive en Corea pero no puede leer lo que ella ha escrito porque no conoce su idioma. El relato se titula *Dear Juno*. Estoy aprendiendo acerca de las diferentes partes del relato: los personajes, el ambiente y el argumento. Estoy prestando atención a estas cosas mientras leo. Quiero conocer mejor a Juno y saber lo que él hace para entender la carta de su abuela.

Destrezas de la semana

Comprensión: personajes, ambiente, argumento

Vocabulario: claves de frase

Ortografía/Fonética: palabras con sonidos de vocales largas como en *make*, *kite* y *hope*

Nombre _____

Sé un autor o autora

Mira la ilustración y luego hablaremos acerca de cómo podríamos usarla para crear un personaje, un ambiente y un argumento. Puedes escribir nuestras decisiones en el anotador.

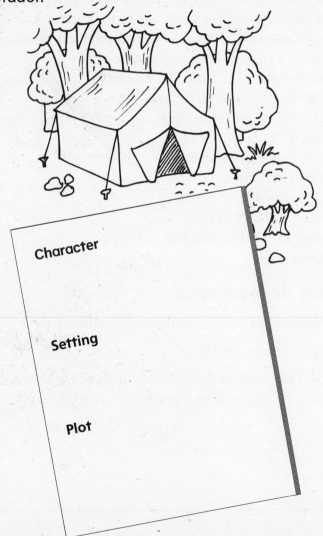

Character

Setting

Plot

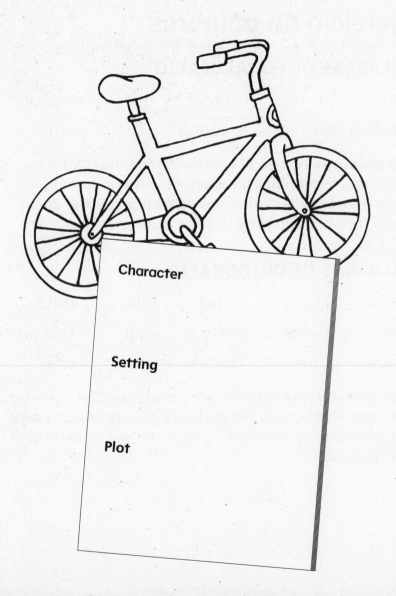

Character

Setting

Plot

Comprehension Check

Retell the Story

Use a Character Web to write down clues that describe the children in the story. Then retell the story.

Think and Compare

1. Reread page 10. Why does Danny feel that the letter from Mr. Addo's class is better than the letter from his class? *(Analyze Character, Setting, and Plot)*

2. If you had a pen pal what would you tell the person about yourself and where you live? *(Synthesize)*

3. What are some of the reasons people write letters? *(Apply)*

Dear Ghana

by Ellen Dreyer
illustrated by Fred Willingham

Table of Contents

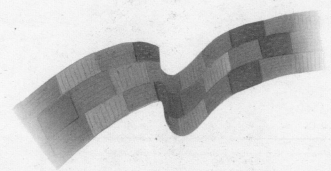

© 2007 Macmillan/McGraw-Hill

Chapter 1

Pen Pal Surprises

Mr. Wilson asked all the children to take their seats. He pulled a world map down over the chalkboard. "Here's the journey our letters will take," he said. He set his fingertip on Iowa City, Iowa.

2

Mr. Addo listened to his excited students. He knew that the two classes would be "pals" for a long time.

15

Two days later, the gifts were ready. The class packed them up. Mr. Wilson added photographs of last year's Harvest Festival.

A week later, the package arrived in Mr. Addo's class. His students loved the gifts. They began to plan for their next package to their new friends.

14

© 2007 Macmillan/McGraw-Hill

His finger soared in a long arc all the way to Ghana, Africa.

"Ghana is many thousands of miles from Iowa," he explained. "Life is very different there."

3

A week earlier, Mr. Wilson had announced that his class was going to become pen pals with a classroom of students in Africa.

Mr. Wilson rolled up the map. He picked up a piece of chalk. "Please raise your hand if you know what you'd like to say in the letter."

He wrote a greeting at the top of the chalkboard.

Dear students of Mr. Addo's class,

Dear students of Mr. Addo's Class,

Thank you for the wonderful gifts! The handmade paper and the kente cloth are beautiful.

We have made some harvest gifts for you. Farmers use scarecrows to keep birds out of their fields. Apple cake is a favorite Harvest Festival treat. And leaves of different colors are seen everywhere now.

In school, we study the same subjects that you do. We have gym class and music class, too. Our favorite sports are soccer, basketball, and baseball.

Sincerely,

The students of Mr. Wilson's Class

Chapter 4
The New Letter

The next morning, Noelle and Danny walked up and down the rows, distributing craft supplies. The children started making colorful, funny scarecrows and colored leaves.

After lunch, the class wrote a new letter.

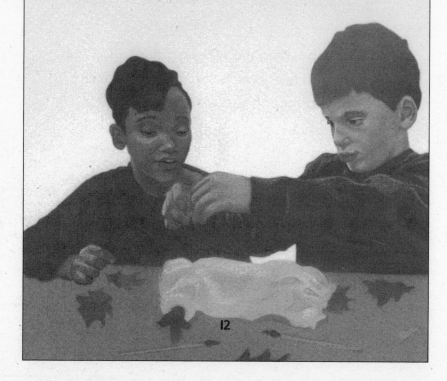

© 2007 Macmillan/McGraw-Hill

Dear Ghana

Danny's hand shot up. "We're very excited to be your pen pals," he said.

Mr. Wilson wrote those words under the greeting.

Then Sonya raised her hand. "It's autumn here in Iowa. What is the weather like now in Ghana?"

Chapter 2
The Letter

The class finished writing the letter. Two of the children copied it onto a clean piece of paper. It read:

Dear students of Mr. Addo's class,

We are very excited to be your pen pals.

It is autumn here in Iowa. What is the weather like now in Ghana? The leaves of our trees turn from green to red and gold. Then they fall from the trees. They crackle when you walk on them.

Soon our town will have a Harvest Festival. People will decorate their yards with corn stalks and pumpkins. Farmers will come from all over Iowa to sell fruits and vegetables. Our class will put on a play for the whole town!

We hope to hear from you soon.

Sincerely,

The students of Mr. Wilson's class

6

"Harvest gifts!" Victor called out.

Mr. Wilson scratched his chin. "Hmmm. Such as...?"

"Scarecrows!"

"Apple cake!"

"Autumn leaves!"

Mr. Wilson laughed. "Great ideas. We can send apple cake and autumn leaves. You can draw or paint some scarecrows too."

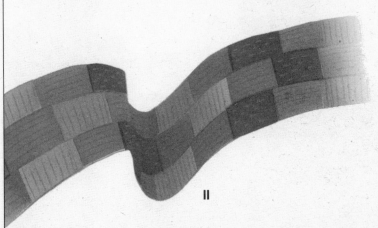

11

"That's a much better letter than the one we sent them," Danny said.

"Why, Danny?" Mr. Wilson asked.

"Well, they told us a lot about themselves. Much more than we told them about us!"

Noelle nodded. "They also sent us some really cool gifts."

In the packages were pieces of bright, handwoven fabric. "This is kente cloth," Mr. Wilson said. "It got its name from 'kenteen,' which means 'basket.'"

Then Danny had an idea. "Maybe we could send some gifts to them."

10

Mr. Wilson took a photograph of the class. He put it into the envelope with the letter. After school, he took the letter to the post office.

Three weeks later, Mr. Wilson's class received a reply. The children from Ghana had sent a package. Inside there was a letter, a set of photographs, and many small packages. There were also some sheets of paper with a starry pattern.

7

© 2007 Macmillan/McGraw-Hill

Chapter 3
The Reply

"Let's read the letter first," Luisa suggested.

Mr. Wilson opened the envelope and handed the letter to her. Luisa read aloud.

Dear students of Mr. Wilson's class,

Odze Ku! That means "hello" in the Ga language. We were delighted to get your letter and the photograph!

Right now it is the rainy season here in Accra, Ghana's capital city.

We do have a harvest celebration called Homowo. During Homowo, we dance, sing, and eat delicious foods.

Our school is in the center of Accra. We learn reading, writing, and math. We also study the traditions of our country. Some of these traditions are included in this package! They are gifts for you, dear pen pals.

Warm wishes,

The students in Mr. Addo's class

Word Workout

WORDS TO KNOW

content   neighborhood   resort   addressing

Double Trouble I'll use one of the words in a sentence. Then you can give me a sentence using the same word but with a different meaning.

SPELLING WORDS

snail	fail	plain	paint	sway
braid	tray	plays	bay	pail
trail	gray	May	ray	great

Win Points I'll give you a word from the list, and you can write it down. Count up how many words have **ay**, **ai**, or neither of those spellings. I'll give you a point for each correct total. Then we'll double-check your spelling list. Did you score 15?

(fold here)

Home-School Connection

Dear Family Member:

Our class is reading about wild animals and where they live. In "Whose Habitat Is It?" the main idea is that some wild animals have lost the places in which they live. People are building houses and roads in the animals' habitats. The details tell more about the main idea. I read about a black bear that tried to break into a man's kitchen window! The bears have lost their own habitat and can't find enough food to eat.

This Week's Skills

Comprehension: main idea and details

Vocabulary: using a dictionary

Spelling/Phonics: the sound of long **a** spelled **ai** and **ay**

Name _____

Flip-Flopping Main Ideas

Here's how to play this game.

• Flip a coin.
• If the coin comes up "heads," use the picture to make up details about the Heads main idea.
• If the coin comes up "tails," use the picture to make up details about the Tails main idea.

Heads: The Jacksons went shopping for a new pet.

Tails: The animals needed more space and a quiet environment.

Heads: The comic book *Mightygirl* is full of action and adventure.

Tails: A film company is making a movie of *Mightygirl*, and they are wondering what kind of girl should star in it.

Heads: It was a bad morning at Mrs. Adorno's day-care center.

Tails: Mr. Adorno, the toymaker, had lots of work to do.

Ejercicio de palabras

PALABRAS DE VOCABULARIO

content   neighborhood   resort   addressing

Tra bajo doble Voy a usar una de las palabras en una oración. Luego, puedes darme otra oración usando la misma palabra pero con otro significado.

PALABRAS DE ORTOGRAFÍA

snail	fail	plain	paint	sway
braid	tray	plays	bay	pail
trail	gray	May	ray	great

Ganar puntos Te voy a dar una palabra de la lista y tú la escribes. Cuenta cuántas palabras se escriben con **ay** o **ai**, o cuántas palabras no se escriben con ninguna de estas dos opciones. Te daré un punto por cada total correcto. Luego, verificaremos tu lista de palabras. ¿Ganaste 15 puntos?

(fold here)

Conexión con el hogar

Queridos familiares:

Nuestra clase está leyendo acerca de los animales salvajes y dónde viven. La idea principal en el artículo *Whose Habitat Is It?* es cómo los animales salvajes perdieron los lugares en donde vivían habitualmente. La gente está construyendo casas y caminos en los hábitats de los animales. Los detalles nos cuentan más sobre la idea principal. ¡Leí sobre un oso negro que trató de entrar a la cocina de una casa por la ventana! Los osos perdieron su propio hábitat y no pueden encontrar alimento suficiente para comer.

Destrezas de la semana

Comprensión: idea principal y detalles

Vocabulario: usar al diccionario

Ortografía/Fonética: el sonido de **a** larga escrito **ai** y **ay**

Nombre _____

Tirar la moneda

Lee a continuación cómo jugar el juego.
- Tira una moneda.
- Si la moneda sale "heads", usa el dibujo para escribir detalles sobre la idea principal que dice "heads".
- Si la moneda sale "tails", usa el dibujo para escribir detalles sobre la idea principal que dice "tails".

Heads: Jack decided to turn the town park into a zoo.

Tails: The animals needed more space and a quiet environment.

Heads: The comic book *Mightygirl* is full of action and adventure.

Tails: A film company is making a movie of *Mightygirl*, and they are wondering what kind of girl should star in it.

Heads: It was a bad morning at Mrs. Adorno's day-care center.

Tails: Mr. Adorno, the toymaker, had lots of work to do.

Comprehension Check

Retell

Look back through the book. Use the pictures to retell the information.

Think and Compare

1. Reread pages 11-12. What are these pages mainly about? What details support the main idea? *(Identify Main Idea and Details)*

2. What plants and animals of the rainforest do you find most interesting? Explain. *(Synthesize)*

3. Why is it important to learn about the rainforest? What do you think people should do to help save rainforests? Why? *(Evaluate)*

© 2007 Macmillan/McGraw-Hill

SAVING THE RAINFOREST

BY TISHA HAMILTON

Table of Contents

Introduction

What is a rainforest? A rainforest is a warm, wet place with many tall trees, vines, and bright flowers. Everywhere you look, there is something wonderful to see and to hear.

Monkeys screech from the trees. Frogs croak and snakes slither on the ground. Tiny birds whiz around. Tree trunks are covered with green vines. The ground is soft and springy.

The rainforest is beautiful. It's also an important part of our world.

Glossary

cacao *(kuh-KAY-oh)* a tree from which cocoa comes *(page 8)*

canopy *(KAN-uh-pee)* an overhead covering *(page 4)*

climate *(KLIGH-mit)* weather over a long period of time *(page 12)*

moisture *(MOYS-chuhr)* water or small drops of water in the air *(page 5)*

oxygen *(OK-suh-juhn)* a gas that we need in order to breathe; plants give off oxygen *(page 6)*

Index

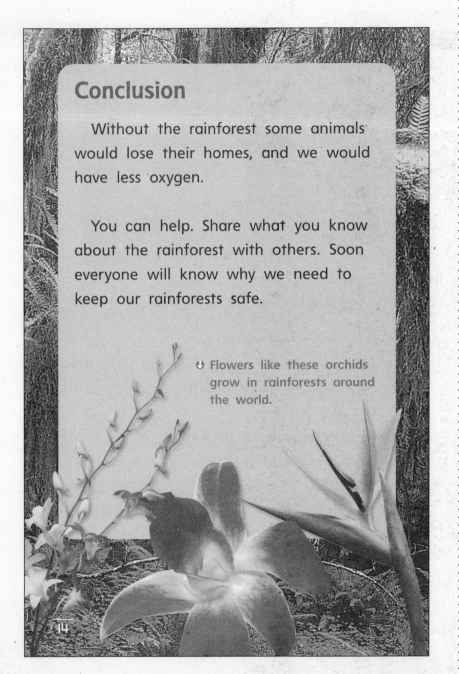

Conclusion

Without the rainforest some animals would lose their homes, and we would have less oxygen.

You can help. Share what you know about the rainforest with others. Soon everyone will know why we need to keep our rainforests safe.

Flowers like these orchids grow in rainforests around the world.

© 2007 Macmillan/McGraw-Hill

This hummingbird lives in the rainforest of Costa Rica.

The screams of the howler monkey can be heard throughout the rainforest.

CHAPTER 1
Look Inside

The rainforest is home to many plants and animals. People live in neighborhoods near the rainforest, too. They all need the rainforest for food and shelter.

If you flew above the rainforest you could not see the ground. This is because the trees form a huge green umbrella over the forest. This is called the **canopy**.

☉ This map shows the world's rainforests. The red line represents the equator. Think of it as a belt around the middle of the Earth. The rainforests are found along that belt.

Equator

4

☉ This man is planting fruit trees to keep the rainforest green.

People have come up with many ways to address this problem. One way to save the forests is to learn all about them.

Another way is to get wood from somewhere else. Now there are tree farms where wood is grown. If you can get trees from a farm, then you don't need to cut down a forest. Cutting a rainforest tree should only be done as a last resort.

13

Saving the Rainforest

Rainforests are home to over half the world's plants and animals. When the rainforest is lost, the circle of life breaks down. The **climate** changes. The plants and animals die off.

↻ These villagers worked with the Nigerian government to save the Ekuri rainforest.

12

When it rains the water hits the tops of the trees. Then it moves down to their roots. In the thick undergrowth the air stays moist. Tree roots drink up the water. Then the water moves up the inside of the trees to the tops. The green leaves give off some of this **moisture** into the air. When there is enough moisture in the air it rains again.

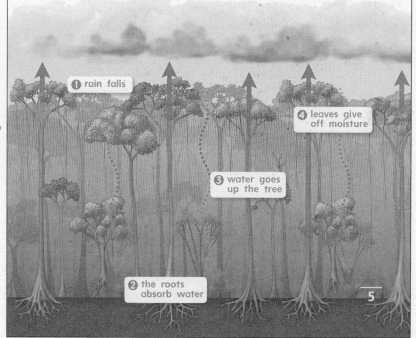

❶ rain falls

❹ leaves give off moisture

❸ water goes up the tree

❷ the roots absorb water

5

CHAPTER 2
Lots of Food

If you were lost in a rainforest you would not go hungry. Oranges, nuts, and many other foods grow there.

Trees and plants in the rainforest give off 20% of the world's **oxygen**. We all need oxygen to live. If trees in the rainforest are cut down, there will be less oxygen to breathe.

↻ Bananas grow in the rainforests.

6

© 2007 Macmillan/McGraw-Hill

CHAPTER 3
Let's Save It!

Once rainforests covered huge areas of the world. Now these forests and their contents are shrinking. People cut down the trees to build homes and to farm. Nearly half of the world's rainforests have been destroyed. They are still being destroyed today.

↻ Workers in the Amazon cut down trees to plant crops.

11

The rainforest provides more than food for the people who live there. Some of the plants are used to make medicines. These medicines save lives.

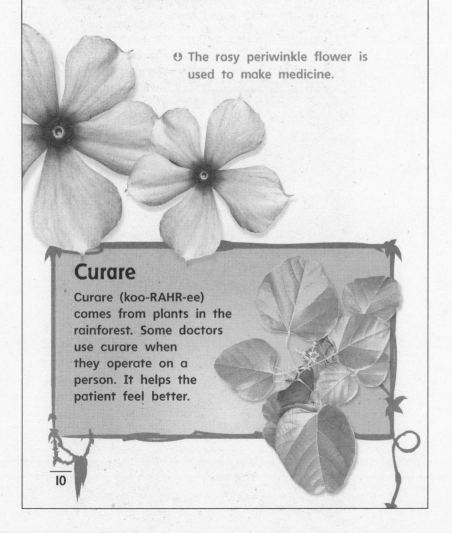

◐ The rosy periwinkle flower is used to make medicine.

Curare

Curare (koo-RAHR-ee) comes from plants in the rainforest. Some doctors use curare when they operate on a person. It helps the patient feel better.

© 2007 Macmillan/McGraw-Hill

The people who live near the rainforests make their homes from wood found there. They also burn the wood to keep warm and to cook their food. They hunt the animals for food. They eat the many foods that grow in the rainforest.

◑ A worker picks and carries the fruit.

◐ The fruit is shipped to stores.

Bananas 69¢ per lb

One big food crop is **cacao**. It grows in and near the forests. You drink it in hot cocoa. It's in candy bars, too.

1 **Blossoms**

2 **Pods**

© 2007 Macmillan/McGraw-Hill

From Cacao to Chocolate

Cacao plants blossom in the cool shade of tall trees. Pods hang from the branches. Inside these pods are seeds. The seeds are dried in the sun until they are dark brown. Then they are ground into powder. This powder is used to make many foods.

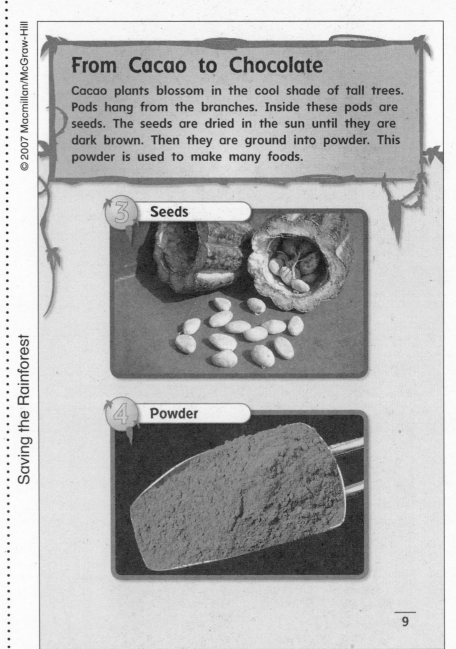

3 **Seeds**

4 **Powder**

Word Workout

WORDS TO KNOW

down   echoes   fierce   huddle

junior   shuffles   whips

Your Own Crossword Make up a crossword puzzle. First fit the words into a grid. Then make up clues. Give it to another family member or a friend. See if they can do the puzzle.

SPELLING WORDS

soak   loaf   float   roast   gold

coast   coal   bowl   slow   grows

show   blow   snow   scold   sold

Spelling Round Try to memorize as many of the spelling words as you can. Then I'll ask for a word with **o, oa,** or **ow**. Spell one of your spelling words for each pattern I give you. Did you get 15 words right? Hurray for you!

(fold here)

Home-School Connection

Dear Family Member:

So far, the pages I have read in the book *Penguin Chick* tell about penguins and penguin eggs. I'm thinking about the main idea and details as I read. I think the main idea of the book will be that father penguins take care of their chicks. The details will tell about this. I'll have to see.

This Week's Skills

Comprehension: main idea and details

Vocabulary: homographs—words spelled the same but with different meanings

Spelling/Phonics: the sound of long **o** spelled **o, ow,** and **oa**

Name _____

Scramble for Details!

The Bears played a very exciting softball game. When you unscramble the letters, you'll find details that tell why the game was exciting.

1. Both _____ were determined to win.

    S M E A T

2. The game was tied in the ninth _____.

    N I N N G I

3. The pitcher threw two _____.

    E S R I K T S

4. The _____ cheered and yelled.

    D R C O W

take me out to the ball game.....

5. Angie knew the Bears were _____ on her.

    N G C O N I U T

6. She stood at the _____ and bent her knees.

    L P E A T

7. The bat _____ and the ball sailed over the fence.

    K D C A R E C

8. They did it! The _____ won the game.

    R E B S A

Answers: teams, inning, strikes, crowd, counting, plate, cracked, bears

44

Ejercicio de palabras

PALABRAS DE VOCABULARIO

down	echoes	fierce	huddle
junior	shuffles	whips	

Tu propio crucigrama Haz un crucigrama. Primero coloca las palabras en una cuadrícula. Luego escribe las pistas. Dáselo a un miembro de tu familia o a un amigo. Fíjate si pueden hacer el crucigrama.

PALABRAS DE ORTOGRAFÍA

soak	loaf	float	roast	gold
coast	coal	bowl	slow	grows
show	blow	snow	scold	sold

Una ronda de ortografía Trata de memorizar la mayor cantidad de las palabras de ortografía como puedas. Luego pediré una palabra con **o, oa** o **ow**. Deletrea una de tus palabras de ortografía para cada pauta que doy. ¿Acertaste 15 palabras? ¡Qué bien!

Conexión con el hogar

Queridos familiares:

Hasta ahora, las páginas que leí del libro *Penguin Chick* hablan acerca de los pingüinos y los huevos de los pingüinos. Mientras leo, pienso acerca de la idea principal y los detalles. Creo que la idea principal del libro será sobre los pingüinos papás que cuidan de sus crías. Los detalles hablarán acerca de esto. Tendré que leer un poco más.

Destrezas de la semana

Comprensión: idea principal y detalles

Vocabulario: homógrafos—palabras que se escriben igual, se pronuncion igual pero tienen diferentes significados

Ortografía/Fonética: el sonido de **o** escrito como **o, ow** y **oa**

Nombre _____

¡Ordenar para encontrar detalles!

El equipo de softball llamado Bears jugó un partido muy emocionante. Cuando ordenes las letras, encontrarás los detalles que dicen por qué el partido fue emocionante.

1. Both _____ were determined to win.

   S M E A T

2. The game was tied in the ninth _____.

   N I N N G I

3. The pitcher threw two _____.

   E S R I K T S

4. The _____ cheered and yelled.

   D R C O W

take me out to the ball game.....

5. Angie knew the Bears were _____ on her.

   N G C O N I U T

6. She stood at the _____ and bent her knees.

   L P E A T

7. The bat _____ and the ball sailed over the fence.

   K D C A R E C

8. They did it! The _____ won the game.

   R E B S A

Comprehension Check

Retell

Use a Main Idea Chart to record details and main ideas about Weddell seals. Tell where the seals live, what helps them live there, and how they get food.

Main Idea	Details

Think and Compare

1. Turn to page 5. What is the first paragraph mostly about? What details support this main idea? *(Identify Main Idea and Details)*

2. What type of protection would you need to live in a cold, icy climate? *(Apply)*

3. Some people want to drill for oil in Antarctica. If this were allowed, how would it affect the Weddell seals? *(Analyze/Synthesize)*

16

The Weddell Seals of Antarctica

by Sandy Riggs

Table of Contents

Introduction

They have soft, golden fur and big flippers. They have bright eyes and whiskers. Sometimes they look like they're smiling. They are Weddell seal pups. And they live in a cold, icy place called Antarctica.

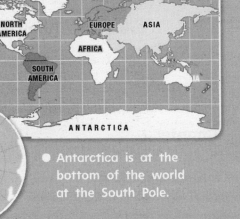

● Antarctica is at the bottom of the world at the South Pole.

2

© 2007 Macmillan/McGraw-Hill

Glossary

mammal *(MAM-mul)* an animal that is warm-blooded, and has a backbone. *(page 5)*

nostril *(NOS-truhl)* an opening in the nose through which a human or animal breathes *(page 8)*

oxygen *(OK-si-juhn)* a gas that all animals need in order to live *(page 12)*

predator *(PRED-uh-tuhr)* an animal that eats other animals *(page 5)*

prey *(PRAY)* an animal that is hunted by another animal for food *(page 11)*

Index

15

Conclusion

Antarctica is an icy place of freezing weather, strong winds, and powerful storms. And Weddell seals have what it takes to live in a frozen land.

14

⌒ Water and ice surround Antarctica.

⌒ Weddell seals live both on ice and under it.

3

CHAPTER 1

Weddell Seal Pups

In September, October, and November, the female Weddell seals come out of the water to give birth to their pups. Each mother has only one pup.

The seals climb onto fast ice, ice that is attached to land. Unlike penguins, they do not form in a huddle. Each one finds a separate place on the ice.

↻ A seal mother lies beside her pup.

4

We are still learning new things about the Weddell seals. Scientists attach small cameras onto the seals. These don't harm the seals or their prey in any way. But the cameras give the scientists a moving picture of the hunters at work.

Fast Fact

Scientists use underwater video cameras to find more about the foods Weddell seals eat.

13

A diving seal goes into deep water.

What if you had to dive in the ocean for your food? How long could you hold your breath? A Weddell seal can stay underwater for over an hour. It does this by keeping **oxygen** in its body. Oxygen is a gas in the air. All animals need oxygen to live.

12

A seal pup weighs about 55 pounds (25 kilograms) at birth. In just ten days, the pup doubles its weight. At seven weeks, it doubles its weight again. How does this happen? Like all **mammals**, the pup drinks milk from its mother's body. But seal milk is special. More than half of it is fat. This helps the baby grow quickly.

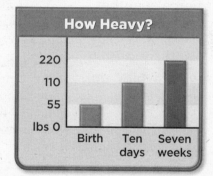

How Heavy?

220		
110		
55		
lbs 0	Birth	Ten days	Seven weeks

After two weeks, the mother gives her pup a swimming lesson in the cold Arctic waters. The pup shuffles to the water's edge. The mother pushes her young one into the water. Soon the pup is swimming.

Fast Fact
The Weddell seals have fierce enemies, or **predators**. Two of these are the killer whale and the leopard seal.

5

CHAPTER 2

Life Under Ice

A Weddell seal's water home is under thick layers of ice. The ice protects seals from Antarctica's fierce weather. During an Antarctic storm, a strong wind whips up enormous waves. Then the ice breaks apart.

Fast Fact
Unlike other Antarctic animals, the Weddell seal does not leave Antarctica during the winter. It doesn't migrate to a warmer

⟳ A Weddell seal comes up for air.

6

The Weddell Seals of Antarctica

⚲ This seal finds food in the cracked ice.

Weddell seals hunt their **prey** in different ways. Sometimes they stalk large prey by swimming very, very quietly. To catch small prey, they blow air into cracks in the ice. Small fish come flying out of the cracks. This is an easy meal for the clever hunters.

Weddell seals also use light for hunting. Sunlight makes the ice shine. After diving deep, a seal may look back up through the water. It may see the shadow of a fish on the ice. If so, it will catch another meal.

II

Getting Food

Like all animals, the Weddell seal needs food to live. What do you think a Weddell seal eats most often? Fish! But it also feeds on squid, octopus, and small sea animals called krill. The seal stays underwater to eat. And it doesn't bother to chew its food. It just bites off big hunks of food and swallows them whole.

Fish

Squid

Seal Food

Octopus

Krill

10

© 2007 Macmillan/McGraw-Hill

The Weddell Seals of Antarctica

An older seal has darker ⤵ fur than a young seal.

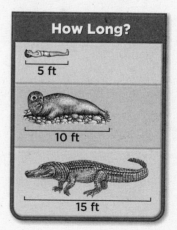

The seals poke their heads through the spaces in the ice to breathe air. While under the water, they hold their breath or breathe through holes in the ice.

What helps the seals live under ice? A penguin has a coat made of feathers called down. A seal's coat is made of fur. The fur protects the seal from cold and water. A pup is born with light-colored fur. In its growing and junior years, the fur darkens. By the time the seal is an adult, the fur is almost black.

How Long?

5 ft

10 ft

15 ft

7

What else is special about the seal's body? Flippers help it swim swiftly and easily. It can close its **nostrils** when it dives into the water. It can see well underwater. And it can feel things with its whiskers.

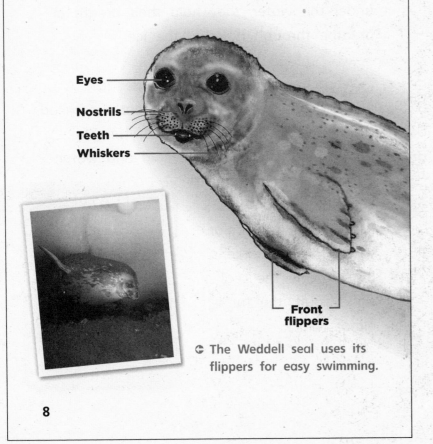

Eyes

Nostrils

Teeth

Whiskers

Front flippers

C The Weddell seal uses its flippers for easy swimming.

Pretend you are standing on top of the ice in Antarctica. You might hear a seal's echoes from across the ice. You might even hear seals calling from under the water. Some calls sound like buzzes. Others sound like loud chirps or whistles. Sometimes the seals make clicking sounds with their teeth. They usually do this "talking" when they are passing each other at a breathing hole. However, the seals are quiet if a killer whale or leopard seal is near.

☝ Predators like this killer whale hunt Weddell seals by listening for their calls.

Back flippers

Word Workout

WORDS TO KNOW

appetite	challenge	healthy	scratch
manage	perfect	satisfy	

TV Ads Let's take a look at each word. What kind of product would use that word in its advertisements? We can make up an ad for each word.

SPELLING WORDS

flight	child	fight	right	tight
bright	might	mild	find	buy
fry	dye	sky	ties	pie

Rhyme and Spell Let's have some fun and use the spelling words to make rhyming sentences. For example, "There's pie in the sky." I'll repeat the rhyming sentence and ask you to spell the rhyming words.

© Macmillan/McGraw-Hill ·····(fold here)·····

Dear Family Member:

The Perfect Pet is a funny story with a problem—Elizabeth wants a pet while her parents do not. I'm learning that many stories begin with a problem and end with a solution. It looks like Elizabeth is very determined and is going to do many things to get a pet. How she makes it happen will be the solution. Whatever happens, I think it will be funny.

This Week's Skills

Comprehension: problem and solution

Vocabulary: words with more than one meaning

Spelling/Phonics: the sound of **i** spelled **i, ie, y,** and **igh**

Name _____

WHAT KIND OF PET?

What pet does each child have? Finish the puzzle to find out.

- Read each clue. When a child does not like a certain animal, write NO in the box for the child's pet.
- When you have three NO's in a row or a column, write YES in the blank box.
- When you have YES in a box, write NO in the boxes for that row and column.

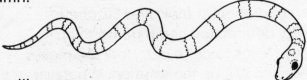

- Rocky does not like cats.
- Claire does not like animals with fur.
- Max only likes animals with four legs.
- Jan is allergic to dogs.
- Claire does not like animals with a shell.
- Max does not want to walk a pet.
- Jan is allergic to cats.
- Rocky does not like animals that eat lettuce.

	dog	cat	snake	turtle
Rocky				
Jan				
Max				
Claire				

Rocky has a _____.

Jan has a _____.

Max has a _____.

Claire has a _____.

Ejercicio de palabras

PALABRAS DE VOCABULARIO

appetite	challenge	healthy
manage	pefect	satisfy

Anuncios publicitarios de televisión Veamos cada una de las palabras. ¿Qué tipo de producto usaría esa palabra en su anuncio publicitario? Podemos crear un anuncio publicitario para cada palabra.

PALABRAS DE ORTOGRAFÍA

flight	child	fight	right	tight
bright	might	mild	find	buy
fry	dye	sky	ties	pie
soak	bowl	gold	wind	children

Rimar y escribir Vamos a divertirnos usando las palabras de ortografía para escribir oraciones que rimen. Por ejemplo: *There's pie in the sky*. No usaré las palabras *soak, bowl* o *gold*. Repetiré la oración que rima y te pediré que deletrees las palabras que riman.

(fold here)

Conexión con el hogar

Queridos familiares:

The Perfect Pet es un cuento divertido pero con un problema: Elizabeth quiere tener una mascota pero sus padres no quieren tener una. Estoy aprendiendo que muchos relatos comienzan con un problema y terminan con una solución. Parece que Elizabeth está muy decidida y va a hacer muchas cosas para conseguir una mascota. La solución será cómo lo logra. Pase lo que pase, creo que será divertido.

Destrezas de la semana

Comprensión: problema y solución

Vocbulario: palabras con más de un significado

Ortografía/Fonética: el sonido de **i** escrito **i, ie, y, igh**

Nombre _____

¿Qué tipo de mascota?

¿Qué tipo de mascota tiene cada niño? Termina el juego para averiguarlo.

- Lee cada pista. Cuando a un niño no le gusta una mascota, escribe NO en la casilla de la mascota del niño.
- Cuando tengas dos NO en una hilera o en una columna, escribe YES en la casilla en blanco.
- Cuando tengas YES en una casilla, escribe NO en todas las casillas de esa hilera o columna.

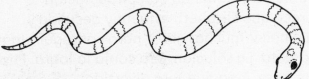

- Rocky does not like cats.
- Claire does not like animals with fur.
- Max doesn't like animals that hiss.
- Jan is allergic to dogs.
- Claire does not like animals with a shell.
- Max does not want to walk a pet.
- Jan is allergic to cats.
- Rocky does not like animals that eat lettuce.

	dog	cat	snake	turtle
Rocky				
Jan				
Max				
Claire				

Rocky has a _____.

Jan has a _____.

Max has a _____.

Claire has a _____.

Comprehension Check

Retell the Story

Use the pictures in the story to retell the story in your own words. Then complete a Problem and Solution Chart. What was Charlie's problem? How did he solve it?

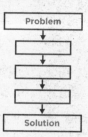

Think and Compare

1. Look back at page 6. What did Emma suggest Charlie do to solve his problem? *(Identify Problem and Solution)*

2. Think of a time you had to prove to a friend or family member that you could do something. How did you do it? *(Synthesize)*

3. What happens to animals if they are not cared for? What can people do to help these animals? *(Apply)*

16

© 2007 Macmillan/McGraw-Hill

Charlie's Pet Problem

by Carrie Smith
illustrated by Gideon Kendall

Table of Contents

Chapter 1
"Mom, I Want a Dog!"

Charlie was almost nine, and he had wanted a pet since he was three. Emma, his best friend, had a dog. Josh had a dog and a cat. And today, Carlos had told him all about his fish. "It just wasn't fair," Charlie thought as he rode the school bus home. Everybody had a pet except him.

When Charlie got off the bus, he went in the house and said, "Mom, I want a dog."

"Well, hello to you too," she said.

Charlie said, "Every one of my friends has a pet, and—"

When Charlie's mother called him to dinner, Winnie came too. She hopped on his lap and purred while he ate.

"Winnie's getting awfully cozy here," said Charlie's mother. "Mrs. Perry had better come home soon."

"She flies home tomorrow," Charlie said sadly.

"Charlie, you've done a good job taking care of Winnie," his mother said. "In fact, you've done such a good job, you deserve a pet of your own. Let's go to the shelter this weekend and pick out a dog."

Charlie smiled. "Or maybe a cat," he said.

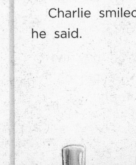

Chapter 4
A Week with Winnie

On Friday after school, Charlie raced up the stairs to his room. There was Winnie lying on the bed. He petted her chin and she purred.

Mrs. Perry had warned Charlie that Winnie might lose her appetite while Mrs. Perry was away. But Winnie had eaten every bowl of food Charlie had given her, including some treats Mrs. Perry had left. Charlie knew he was keeping the cat healthy.

Charlie's Pet Problem

"Look, Charlie! We have talked about this before and we agree that a dog is a big responsibility."

"I know," said Charlie.

"A dog needs to be fed and walked every day," his mother said. "A dog is not a toy you can suddenly decide you're tired of. Are you sure you can manage all that?"

Charlie said, "Yes, I'm sure."

His mother sighed. Charlie could tell she was thinking. He held his breath. "Please say yes," he thought.

Finally she spoke. "If you really want a dog, you're going to have to prove to me that you are responsible."

Charlie wanted to say, "Prove it how?" But he knew she had given him a challenge, and it was up to him to find a way to convince her.

4

Charlie's Pet Problem

13

He realized that Mrs. Perry was going to ask him to take care of her cat. He liked dogs, not cats. All cats could do was scratch and purr. There was no way he was going to take care of a cat.

He was about to make up an excuse, but then he looked at Mrs. Perry's face. She had a very kind face. He felt sorry for her and found himself saying, "I'll do it."

Mrs. Perry looked relieved. "You don't think your mother would mind? You'd have to come over twice each day, because Winnie gets upset when she's left alone."

Charlie realized that Winnie might be the perfect solution to his problem. "What if I kept her at my house?" he suggested. "Then she wouldn't get lonely. I'll ask my mom if it's okay."

© 2007 Macmillan/McGraw-Hill

Charlie's Pet Problem

She hadn't said no, after all, so there was still hope. But how could he prove he could take care of a dog when he didn't have one?

Chapter 2
Pet Research

Charlie called Emma. "I've got a problem," he told her as soon as she picked up the phone. "How can I show my mom I can take care of a pet?"

"Hmmm...," said Emma. "What if you did some research on pets?"

"Yeah, I could do that," he said.

Mrs. Perry explained that her sister in Dallas was sick. "I'm flying down to see her today. I have to leave soon and the kennel is closed. I have no one to take care of Winnie."

"Winnie?"

"My cat." Mrs. Perry pointed down at the cat carrier at her feet.

Chapter 3
Mrs. Perry's Problem

Charlie was about to go back inside when Mrs. Perry pulled into the driveway next door and waved at him. She'd never been very friendly before. In fact, she sometimes acted as if he wasn't there. Charlie thought she didn't like kids.

Now she got out of her car and walked toward him. "I've got a problem," she said.

Charlie just looked at her. He wanted to say, "You have a problem? Well, I've got a problem too!" Instead he said, "What's wrong?"

10

© 2007 Macmillan/McGraw-Hill

"Listen," Emma said. "Lucy needs a bath. She keeps scratching her fur and I'm worried that she has fleas. Let's talk about this tomorrow, okay?"

Charlie called Josh. Josh said, "I can't talk. I'm feeding Prince. I can't believe this dog's appetite! If I don't get this food in his bowl, I'm afraid he's going to cook for himself."

Charlie thought about calling Carlos, but with his luck Carlos would be cleaning his fish tank. Instead Charlie went outside.

Mr. Perez, a neighbor, was passing by with his dog Sam. Suddenly Charlie had a brilliant idea. He could interview Mr. Perez and tell his mother everything he had learned. This would show her that he was responsible.

8

"Mr. Perez," he called out. "Can I walk with you? I want to ask you some questions."

Mr. Perez glanced at his watch. "Sorry, Charlie. Sam's been in the house all day and he really needs a walk. I am in a rush now, so I have to walk him fast. Can you stop by tomorrow?"

"Sure," said Charlie. He watched as Mr. Perez led Sam down the block.

This was hopeless, Charlie thought. He would never be able to prove to his mother that he was responsible enough to care for a dog. How could he satisfy her?

9

Word Workout

WORDS TO KNOW

darkened	decorated	gnaws
securing	symbol	weakest

My Week I will choose a word for you from the words above and put it in a sentence. Tell me what the word means. Then choose a word and include it in a summary of something that happened to you this week.

SPELLING WORDS

bean	seal	team	cream	field
clean	weak	freeze	week	creek
heel	street	green	free	speaks

Speed Spell I'll say each word from the list for you to spell. I'll give you five seconds to spell each word correctly. If you misspell a word, I'll say "EEK!" so you have a chance to spell it again.

Home-School Connection

Dear Family Member:

This week we are reading a play called *The Strongest One*. The characters are ants! Little Red Ant is the main character. Little Red Ant's goal is to find out who is the strongest one in the world. He asks different animals if they are the strongest. One by one they tell him of another animal or thing that is stronger. I can tell you this short version of the play because I can summarize. I take the main idea of the play and use the most important details to tell about it.

This Week's Skills

Comprehension: summarize

Vocabulary: antonyms—words that are opposites

Spelling/Phonics: the sound of **e** spelled **ee, ea,** and **ie,** as in *week* and *bean*

Name _____

Short Story

Let's make up a short story together. We've got a character and a setting. We need a plot, events, and a solution. We can write our thoughts here.

Character: Betty Bird, a robin who lives in the forest
Setting: a forest

Problem

Plot

Events

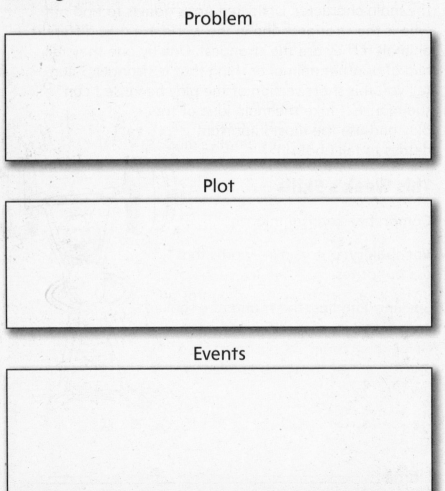

Solution

And Shorter

Now it's time to make a short story shorter. Let's time how long it takes us to summarize our story.

Ejercicio de palabras

PALABRAS DE VOCABULARIO

darkened	decorated	gnaws
securing	symbol	weakest

Mi semana Voy a escoger una palabra para ti de la lista de palabras de arriba y la pondré en una oración. Dime el significado de la palabra. Luego escoge una palabra e inclúyela en un resumen de algo que te haya pasado durante esta semana.

PALABRAS DE ORTOGRAFÍA

bean	seal	team	cream	field
clean	weak	freeze	week	creek
heel	street	green	free	speaks

Ortografía veloz Voy a leer en voz alta cada palabra de la lista para que la deletrees. Te daré cinco segundos para deletrear cada palabra correctamente. Si la deletreas incorrectamente, diré "EEK"! para que tengas otra oportunidad.

Conexión con el hogar

Queridos familiares:

Esta semana estamos leyendo una obra de teatro que se llama *The Strongest One*. ¡Los personajes son hormigas! Little Red Ant es el personaje principal y su objetivo es averiguar quién es el animal más fuerte en el mundo. Le pregunta a diferentes animales si ellos son los más fuertes. Cada uno le dice que hay otro animal que es más fuerte. Te puedo contar esta versión corta de la obra de teatro porque sé cómo resumir. Tomo la idea principal de la obra de teatro y uso los detalles más importante para contar la obra.

Destrezas de la semana

Comprensión: resumir

Vocabulario: antónimos—palabras que son opuestas

Ortografía/Fonética: el sonido de **e** escrito **ee**, **ea** y **ie**, como en *week* y *bean*

Nombre_____

Cuento corto

Escribamos juntos un cuento corto. Ya tenemos un personaje y un ambiente. Necesitamos un argumento, sucesos y una solución. Podemos escribir nuestras ideas a continuación.

Character: Betty Bird, a robin who lives in the forest
Setting: a forest

Problem

Plot

Events

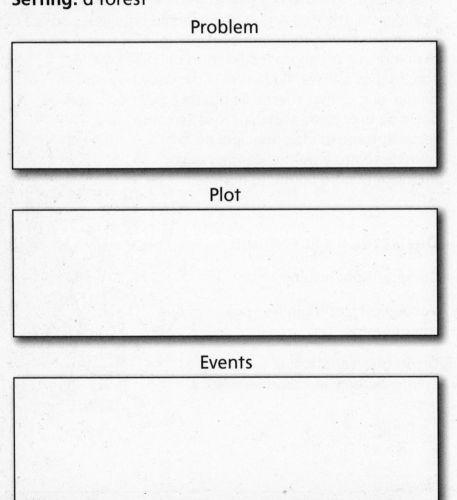

Solution

Y más corto

Ahora hagamos un cuento corto más corto. Veamos cuánto tiempo nos toma resumir nuestro cuento.

Comprehension Check

Summarize the Story

Use a Story Map to list the characters, setting, and events of the story. Then use the map to summarize the story.

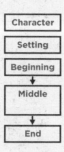

| Character |
| Setting |
| Beginning |
| ↓ |
| Middle |
| ↓ |
| End |

Think and Compare

1. Look back at page 4. What happens to Anna and Maria? *(Summarize)*

2. John makes Maria believe that it can rain pancakes and that there are fish that can walk. Have you ever believed something that you found out later wasn't true? How did you feel when you learned you were wrong? *(Evaluate)*

3. John tells fibs to carry out his plan to save the treasure for the villagers. Should people tell fibs? What problems could come from this? *(Evaluate)*

16

Clever John

Clever John

**told by Sheila Black
illustrated by Anton Petrov**

Table of Contents

Characters:

Narrator

John

Maria

Anna
(Maria's best friend)

Peter
(Anna's husband)

King George
(a greedy man)

2

Clever John

15

Maria: Well, then we had to get the fish out of the rabbit traps.

King George: Fish? You mean rabbits.

Maria: Oh king, you must know that this area is famous for walking fish. Then we had to stop to get the water rabbits out of our nets.

King George: Water rabbits! Don't tell me! I suppose that you found a buried trunk full of gold coins.

Maria: But that's exactly what happened!

Narrator: So, greedy King George went away. He never learned about the sudden good fortune of the people in the village. As for Maria, she still loved to talk, but she did learn how to keep a secret or two.

© 2007 Macmillan/McGraw-Hill

Clever John

Scene 1
John's Problem

Show a backdrop of a village. John, Maria, and other villagers are onstage.

Narrator: John lived in Russia in a village near the castle of a great and greedy king.

King George: Get to work! And you there—weren't you supposed to trap ten rabbits?

John: Yes, oh king.

Narrator: Despite the greedy king, John was happy with his life, except for one thing. His wife, Maria, who was very kindhearted, had a problem. She loved to talk.

Maria: Good morning, Anna!

Anna: Look, I just finished knitting Peter a beautiful new sweater decorated with his favorite birds. But shhh! The sweater is a secret.

Maria: I won't tell a soul.

Anna smiles as Peter walks up.

Peter: Hello, Anna. Hello, Maria.

Maria: Oh, Peter. You'll never guess— Anna knitted you a new sweater for your birthday and it's—.

Anna: Maria! How could you?

Anna stomps offstage with Peter.

4

Narrator: Once one person learned the secret, it did not take long for everyone to learn it, even the king.

King George: What's this I hear about buried treasure? I demand to be told all about it! At once!

Maria: If you insist, oh king. It happened like this. My husband told me about the treasure and we went into the woods to bring it home. First, we came to a tree all covered with pancakes.

King George: Pancakes! What happened next?

13

Scene 3
Maria Tells the Secret

The village

Narrator: Maria promised not to tell a soul about the treasure. Of course, she meant to keep her promise, but the next morning her friend, Anna, came to visit.

Anna: Maria, thank you for the present. I want us to be friends again, even if you are a blabbermouth.

Maria: I am not a blabbermouth. I can keep a secret. In fact, I have a secret right now that I am not going to tell anybody. It's a very big secret. Yesterday, John found a trunk full of gold in the woods.

Anna: A treasure?

Maria: Oops!

Stage is darkened. When lights come on, backdrop is of the woods.

Narrator: One evening when John was out in the woods digging up the roots of an old tree for King George, his shovel hit something hard.

John: What's this? An old trunk with a mysterious symbol on it! Oh goodness, it's a pile of gold coins— really buried treasure!

Narrator: John danced for joy, but then he realized he had a big problem.

John: If the king finds out about this treasure, he will keep all of it. If I tell Maria about it, she will tell the whole world.

Narrator: John thought of a plan to fool the king and keep the treasure for the villagers. His plan required pancakes.

Scene 2
A Clever Plan

The village

Maria: Good evening, husband. The pancakes for your dinner are ready. I am going to Anna's house to bring her this present.

John: Go ahead, wife. I'll eat dinner by myself, for I still have work to do this evening. Let's meet later at the edge of the woods. I have something to show you.

John: We'll have a good supper, even if we don't find the treasure.

Maria: But we will find it, won't we?

John: Why, yes. In fact, here it is. A trunk full of gold coins just as if it were left here by the elves!

Narrator: When Maria saw the treasure, she was overjoyed. John loaded the coins into the sack on his back. And he and Maria went home full of plans for what they would do with the money.

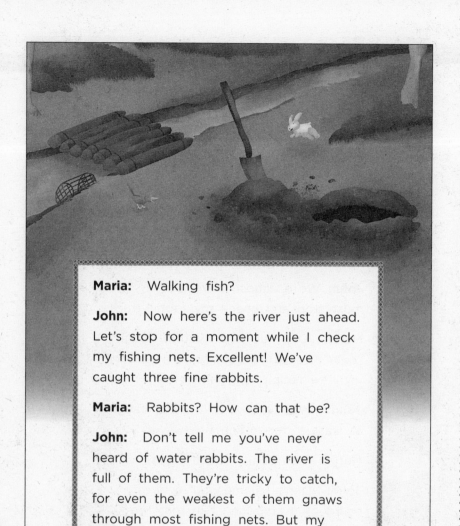

Maria: Walking fish?

John: Now here's the river just ahead. Let's stop for a moment while I check my fishing nets. Excellent! We've caught three fine rabbits.

Maria: Rabbits? How can that be?

John: Don't tell me you've never heard of water rabbits. The river is full of them. They're tricky to catch, for even the weakest of them gnaws through most fishing nets. But my nets can hold the strongest of water rabbits!

Maria: Really?

10

Clever John

Stage darkens. Lights come back on to show the woods.

Narrator: For the next hour, John ran about doing all kinds of mysterious things.

John: First, I must hang these pancakes in this tree. Next, I must put the rabbits from my rabbit trap in my fishing nets, and put the fish from my fishing nets in my rabbit traps. When I'm done securing the rabbit traps with the fish inside, I'll go meet Maria!

Maria calls.

Maria: John, where are you?

7

John: Right here. Are you ready?

Maria: Oh, yes. Will you show me the secret now?

John: When I was digging up a tree for King George, I found a trunk filled with gold coins.

Maria: A treasure!

John: Yes, but we must go and fetch it now when no one will see us. You mustn't tell anyone. Promise?

Maria nods and they walk until they come to a tree hung with pancakes.

Maria: John, there are pancakes growing in that tree!

8

© 2007 Macmillan/McGraw-Hill

Clever John

John: Don't be silly. Pancakes don't grow in trees. They landed there from that big pancake cloud that just passed overhead. It was raining pancakes just a few minutes ago.

Maria: I didn't notice. I suppose I was daydreaming, thinking about what we will do with the treasure.

John: We're almost there, but first I must stop and check my rabbit traps.

Maria: Oh, I do hope you've caught some nice plump rabbits so I can try my new recipe for rabbit stew.

John: What luck! Look, we've caught at least a dozen fine fish.

Maria: Fish in the rabbit traps?

John: Don't tell me you've never heard of the walking fish that live around these parts.

9

Word Workout

WORDS TO KNOW

ached	admire
bothering	concentrate
dangerous	passion
splendid	

Double Check Let's think of a person or a character in a book or a movie. I'll give you a word, and you can put it in a sentence that describes the character.

SPELLING WORDS

lunch	hatch	bench	watching	chick
chunk	much	cheek	chum	cheese
pitch	stretch	ditch	crunching	teacher

Tongue-Twisters Do you know the famous tongue-twister, "How much wood would a woodchuck chuck if a woodchuck could chuck wood?" Let's try to make tongue-twisters with some of your spelling words.

(fold here)

© Macmillan/McGraw-Hill

Home-School Connection

Dear Family Member:

This week our class is reading a fantasy titled *Wolf!* It's a story about a pig, a duck, a cow, and a wolf who read books. I know this story is a fantasy because animals cannot talk and read books. It's different from other books I've read. Other books are about things that can really happen. They are reality books. In books like this one, an author could write about anything he or she imagined.

This Week's Skills

Comprehension: fantasy and reality

Vocabulary: words with more than one meaning

Spelling/Phonics: words with the letters **ch**

Name _____

Real to Ridiculous

Let's play a game. We'll take turns tossing a penny on the page. The picture closest to the penny is the idea for a story. We'll each make up a realistic story or a fantasy based on the picture. Then we'll trade stories with each other.

Ejercicio de palabras

PALABRAS DE VOCABULARIO

ached   admire

bothering   concentrate

dangerous   passion

splendid

Verificar Pensemos en una persona o en un personaje de un libro o una película. Te daré una palabra para que la uses en una oración que describa al personaje.

PALABRAS DE ORTOGRAFÍA

lunch	hatch	bench	watching	chick
chunk	much	cheek	chum	cheese
pitch	stretch	ditch	crunching	teacher

Trabalenguas He aquí un trabalenguas famoso: How much wood would a woodchuck chuck if a woodchuck could chuck wood? ¿Lo conoces? Intentemos escribir un trabalenguas con algunas de tus palabras de ortografía.

{fold here}

© Macmillan/McGraw-Hill

Queridos familiares:

Esta semana nuestra clase está leyendo una fábula titulada *Wolf*! Es un cuento acerca de un puerco, un pato, una vaca y un lobo que leen libros. Sé que este relato es una fábula porque los animales no pueden hablar ni leer libros. Es diferente de otros libros que he leído. Otros libros son acerca de cosas que ocurren en la realidad. Estos libros se llaman libros realistas. En libros como *Wolf!*, el autor puede escribir acerca de cualquier cosa que él o ella haya imaginado.

Destrezas de la semana

Comprensión: fantasía y realidad

Vocabulario: palabras con más de un significado

Ortografía/Fonética: palabras con las letras **ch**

Nombre _____

De real a ridículo

Vamos a jugar un juego. Tomaremos turnos tirando una moneda de un centavo sobre esta página. El dibujo que esté más cerca de la moneda es la idea para el cuento. Escribe un cuento realista o una fábula basado en el dibujo. Luego, intercambiaremos nuestros cuentos.

Comprehension Check

Summarize

Use a Fantasy and Reality Chart to tell about the events and characters in the story. Then use the chart to summarize the story.

Fantasy	Reality

Think and Compare

1. Read the story again. When could you first tell that the story was a fantasy? Give examples. *(Distinguish Between Fantasy and Reality)*

2. What do you admire most about your grandparents or other older relatives? Explain. *(Evaluate)*

3. Why is it important to know exactly who you are chatting with on the Internet? *(Apply)*

16

Katie and the Wolf

by Megan Howard
illustrated by John Nez

Table of Contents

CHAPTER 1
Dinner with Granny

"You haven't eaten any lunch, Katie," my grandmother said. She was right. The pile of mashed potatoes was a round ball. My broccoli pieces still looked like perfect little trees. And I had eaten only a spoonful of bean chili.

The next day, Granny was leaving on a trip to Europe. She was staying on a sheep farm in Ireland for a month. Traveling the world was Granny's passion, but I was worried.

2

I tried to concentrate on the photograph. I thought and thought. It was a wolf!

I jumped up from the computer. Dad called the police, and we both went over to Granny's house.

I was right! Two police officers were walking out of Granny's house with a wolf in handcuffs.

When I got back home, I found an e-mail from Granny. "Katie, I miss you so much. So far I have seen a lot of sheep. Luckily, there haven't been any wolves."

15

"Granny, your eyes look huge," I typed.

"That's just because I'm sick," she wrote back.

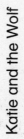

"And your nose looks so long," I pointed out.

"You don't have to insult me," she responded.

"Your teeth are incredibly pointy," I said.

"Those are my new false teeth," she explained.

But there was one feature that made no sense at all. "What about the fur all over your face?"

Ima Wolf logged off right away. There was someone in Granny's house, but it wasn't Granny!

14

© 2007 Macmillan/McGraw-Hill

"With all those sheep, there might be wolves," I told her. "It could be dangerous."

"You've been reading too many fairy tales," Granny said.

I had read plenty of fairy tales. But I had also read a lot of nonfiction. I knew the difference. In fact, I had learned a lot about sheep. "Wolves eat sheep all the time."

"That does sound awful," Granny said with a smile. She was a vegetarian and never ate meat. "I promise to watch out for wolves."

I felt better. I hadn't meant to worry Granny, but I wanted her to be careful.

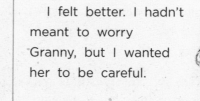

3

After our meal, we cleared the table and washed the dishes.

"I'll mail you lots of postcards from Ireland," Granny told me.

"And you'll e-mail me every night, right?" I asked.

"Of course," she replied. Even though Granny lived right next door, she always sent me a goodnight e-mail.

"I really admire the way you explore the world," I told her. "I hope I grow up to be just like you."

Suddenly, I felt soft fur twisting around my ankles. It was Granny's cat, Ribbon. I picked up Ribbon. "I'll take good care of her," I said.

4

A photo of Ribbon appeared on my computer.

"Maybe it really is Granny after all," I said. We had to know for sure. We needed more proof.

Just then I had a splendid idea! I told her to send me a photograph of herself. I waited until a picture appeared in front of me. It was very blurry. I could hardly see the face.

13

CHAPTER 3
The Girl Who Cried "Wolf!"

Dad and I came up with a plan. If Ima Wolf was Granny, she'd be able to send us a photograph of something in her house.

"Granny, would you send me a picture of Ribbon?"

"I don't have any ribbon," she responded.

Ima Wolf had fallen right into our trap! Granny would have known what I meant.

"Ribbon is your cat," I wrote her.

"Oh, right. I guess I forgot because I'm sick."

"I guess a really sick person could have gotten confused," I said to Dad.

"I know you will," said Granny. "Now run home and do your homework. You have school tomorrow. And I have to pack and make a list of things to do on my trip. Bundle up. It's raining hard."

I put Ribbon on the floor. I pulled on my red raincoat and boots. Then I ran out the door and next door to my house.

© 2007 Macmillan/McGraw-Hill

Katie and the Wolf

IMA Wolf: I'm also hungry

Love2Read: I'll bring you something to eat. What do you want?

IMA Wolf: Lamb stew

"I'm also hungry," came up on the screen right away.

"I'll bring you something to eat," I wrote. "What do you want?"

"Lamb stew," was the response.

Granny never ate meat! Was someone trying to trick me? I looked over at Dad.

"Let's find out what's going on," he said.

11

"Yes," was the answer.

"How are you?" I asked.

The reply came back quickly. "Hungry."

"How is your vacation?"

Her answer surprised me. "I'm not on vacation. I'm home."

What was going on? "Why are you there?" I asked.

"Because I'm sick."

Sick? Poor Granny! "You should have called Dad," I wrote. "He would have helped you."

10

CHAPTER 2
Ima Wolf

The next afternoon, I raced home from school. By the time I got home, my legs ached. Still, I rushed to the computer. My father was already working on it.

"Can I check to see if Granny sent me an e-mail?" I asked without bothering to take my backpack off.

"I have to work, honey," he said.

"What if something funny happened on the plane? She'll want to tell me," I said.

7

My father made room for me at the desk. "All right," he said, "Let's check your messages now."

Dropping my backpack on the floor, I sat down at the computer. There were no new messages. I decided to wait a little while. Maybe Granny just needed more time.

Suddenly, a message popped up on the screen. The screen name was Ima Wolf. "Hi," the message said.

I laughed. It had to be Granny. She was joking about wolves.

I typed a response. "Granny, is that you?"

Word Workout

WORDS TO KNOW

computers   entertainment

objects   predictions

Computer Chat Let's discuss the meanings of these words. Then we can use them to talk about some facts and opinions about computers.

SPELLING WORDS

thick	whales	shock	what	wheel
truth	this	dishpan	washing	month
weather	sixth	pathway	them	fish

Spelling Bee First, you'll give me the spelling words to spell. Then it will be my turn to ask you to spell the words. We'll see if there are some words you need to work on!

(fold here)

Home-School Connection

Dear Family Member:

We're reading a fascinating article titled "What's in Store for the Future?" It talks about things that have already happened. We went into space in rockets, and many people now use cellular phones. These are facts. But the article makes some predictions, also. Those are opinions. Perhaps all cars will be electric. Maybe we will grow all our own food in our own gardens. We can't prove those things, however. If they come true, we're in for a good time!

This Week's Skills

Comprehension: fact and opinion

Vocabulary: plural endings

Spelling/Phonics: words with the letters **th, ph, wh,** and **sh**

Name _____

Scorecard: Fact or Opinion?

Keiji and Chloe sent e-mails to each other one afternoon.
Which child sent the most facts?
Which child sent the most opinions?

CHLOE: 8 + 8 = 16 / I like your sneakers.

KEIJI: The best sneakers are white.

CHLOE: There are many kinds of sneakers. / The Cubs won today's game.

KEIJI: The pitcher threw 12 strikes. / Her picture was on TV.

CHLOE: They predict rain for tomorrow's game.

KEIJI: I think rain is a good change now and then.

CHLOE: I've got a 12-page story to read for homework. / I don't think I'll finish it.

KEIJI: I've got 2 pages of math homework. / Math is hard.

Who gives the most facts?

How many?

Who gives the most opinions?

How many?

Ejercicio de palabras

PALABRAS DE VOCABULARIO

computers   entertainment

objects   predictions

Charla por computadora Hablemos acerca del significado de estas palabras. Luego, las usaremos para hablar acerca de algunos hechos y opiniones sobre las computadoras.

PALABRAS DE ORTOGRAFÍA

thick	whales	shock	what	wheel
truth	this	dishpan	washing	month
weather	sixth	pathway	them	fish

Concurso de ortografía Primero, me darás las palabras de ortografía para deletrear. Luego, será mi turno para pedirte que deletrees las palabras. ¡Vamos a ver si hay algunas palabras en las que tengas que trabajar un poco!

© Macmillan/McGraw-Hill

(fold here)

Conexión con el hogar

Queridos familiares:

Estamos leyendo un artículo fascinante titulado *What's in Store for the Future?* Habla acerca de cosas que ya han pasado. Ya hemos ido al espacio en naves espaciales y mucha gente ahora usa teléfonos celulares. Estos son hechos. Pero el artículo hace también algunas predicciones. Ésas son opiniones. Quizás todos los automóviles sean eléctricos. Posiblemente cultivemos nuestros propios alimentos en nuestras propias granjas. Sin embargo, no podemos comprobar esas cosas. Si se hacen realidad, ¡lo pasaremos muy bien!

Destrezas de la semana

Comprensión: hecho y opinión

Vocabulario: fines plurales

Ortografía/Fonética:
palabras con las letras **th, ph, wh** y **sh**

Nombre _____

Anotador: ¿Hecho u opinión?

Keiji y Chloe se enviaron correos electrónicos durante toda una tarde. ¿Qué niño envió más hechos? ¿Qué niño envió más opiniones?

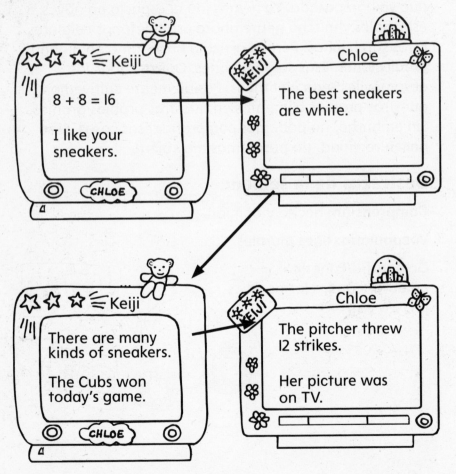

Who gives the most facts?

How many?

Who gives the most opinions?

How many?

Comprehension Check

Summarize

Use the photos in the book to summarize the information in the text.

Think and Compare

1. Turn to page 10 in this book. How are computers used for work? Why do you think most people feel computers help them do their work? *(Evaluate Fact and Opinion)*

2. What is your favorite type of computer entertainment? Why? *(Synthesize)*

3. Have computers made our world better or worse? Explain your answer based on what you have learned in this book. *(Evaluate)*

Incredible Inventions: Computers

by Thom Anthony

Table of Contents

Introduction

Take a look around you. Do you see any **computers**? Computers can be found at home or school. They help make clocks and traffic lights work. They are inside watches and cars, and many other objects.

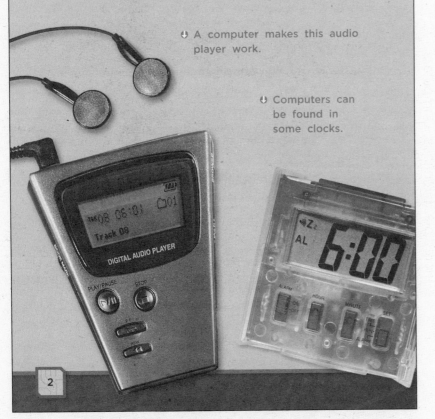

↻ A computer makes this audio player work.

↻ Computers can be found in some clocks.

2

Glossary

abacus *(AB-uh-kuhs)* a tool for solving math problems by using rods and beads *(page 4)*

computer *(kuhm-PYEW-tuhr)* an electronic machine that can store, retrieve, and process information *(page 2)*

Internet *(IN-tuhr-net)* a network that connects computers all over the world *(page 11)*

laptop *(LAP-top)* a computer that is easy to carry from place to place *(page 9)*

microchip *(MIGH-kruh-chip)* a very small device that helps computers run faster *(page 8)*

slide rule *(SLIGHD REWL)* a tool for solving math problems by using rulers *(page 5)*

Index

15

Conclusion

The abacus and the slide rule were once the best tools for working on number problems. Now we have computers that can solve these problems and do so much more. Computers make work faster and easier, help us stay in touch with other people, and provide many forms of entertainment.

In the future, computers will be able to do even more amazing things. We can already predict what some of these things might be. But we will continue to be surprised by these incredible machines.

⟳ This Mars Exploration Rover was developed by NASA. It contains many small powerful computers.

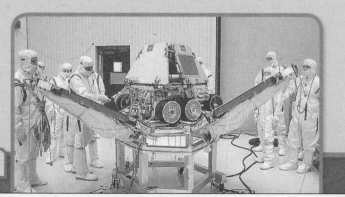

⟳ The shape of this computer keyboard was designed for easy use.

Computers can be used in an office for work. But they can also be used at home for fun. You can play games and songs on a computer. You can make art and music on one too. Learning about what a computer can do can be as much fun as using one. So, get ready to read about how computers have changed our lives.

Chapter I
Life Before Computers

One of the first things people made to help them keep track of numbers was called an **abacus**. It is made of rods and beads. By sliding the beads on the rods, people can do arithmetic. The Chinese abacus was first made about 5000 years ago. It is still used in some parts of China and Japan.

↻ This is an abacus.

4

This face was ➲ created on a computer.

There are many predictions about the future of computers. Most people agree that progress will be made in the way computers look and in the way people will use them.

Some experts think that hand held computers will take the place of books. Others think we'll have computers we can wear. Some may hook on to eyeglasses. This would help pilots. They will be able to look at the sky and see their gauges at the same time. Computers sewn in jackets will let people keep track of their heart rate.

Computer screens that show 3-D images are predicted too. This will make game playing far more exciting.

13

Chapter 4
Today and Tomorrow

Today, computers can do some amazing things. Think about action movies with special effects. Often the creatures or places that you see on the screen are not real, but they sure look like they are. In films animals or robots move and talk like humans. They live in the future or the past. Filmmakers use computers to add special effects to a movie after it has been filmed.

Did You Know...

Filmmakers are not the only people who can use special effects. You can do it too. New digital cameras use computers to take pictures. Once the pictures are on the computer, special programs can change them by adding graphics, changing color and size, and much more.

12

Amazing Inventions:
The Calculator

A calculator is a small machine that does math. You can use it to add, subtract, and much more.

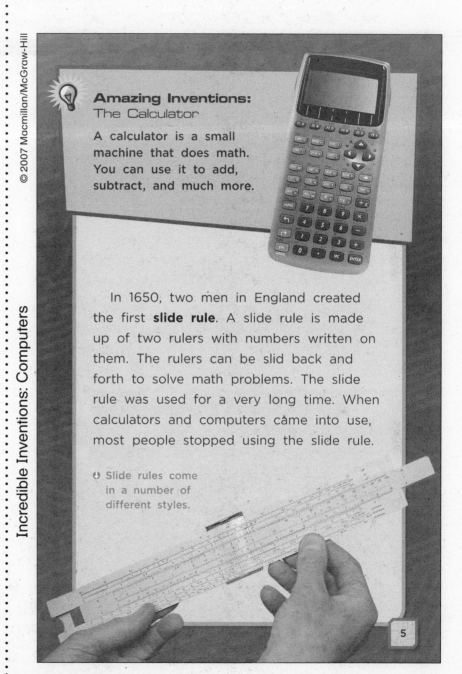

In 1650, two men in England created the first **slide rule**. A slide rule is made up of two rulers with numbers written on them. The rulers can be slid back and forth to solve math problems. The slide rule was used for a very long time. When calculators and computers came into use, most people stopped using the slide rule.

↻ Slide rules come in a number of different styles.

5

Chapter 2
The First Computers

One of the first computers was called the ENIAC. It was completed in 1946 and it was very big. ENIAC weighed as much as seven elephants and took up as much room as a house. Six people were needed to keep it working. It could perform about 500 addition and 300 multiplication problems per second.

☉ The letters ENIAC stand for Electronic Numerical Integrator and Computer.

6

Computer Words

Computers have given new meanings to many familiar words. Think about how the meanings of these words have been changed by computers.

snail mail	memory	net
chat	mouse	crash

The **Internet** is a way to connect to the rest of the world. Using a computer, you can find all kinds of facts. With e-mail or on-line messaging you can keep in touch with friends. You can send photos and make phone calls. A small camera can even let you see the person you're talking to. You also can use the Internet to buy or sell things.

People can ➲ write to each other using e-mail.

11

Now people use computers to do all sorts of work. Doctors use them to find out about health problems. They keep records on computers too.

Repair workers use computers to find problems. They can fix things faster once they know what is wrong.

Writers use computers to create books. Artists and musicians use them too.

Most people think computers make their work easier.

Amazing Inventions:
The First Video Game

Computers have changed the way we play. The first video game was created in 1958. It was called "Tennis for Two." The game was a video version of... you guessed it... tennis!

Early computers had a lot of problems. They could only do one thing at a time. It cost a lot of money to build one. Early computers also took up a lot of space and created a lot of heat. They could break down easily.

This early computer cost $20,000.

Soon, smaller computers that could fit inside a home or an office were built. But they were still slow and expensive. So most people did not buy them. But people wanted to have them and soon they would be able to.

Chapter 3
Modern Computers

In the 1970s, a new, small device called the **microchip** increased the speed of computers. Now people could buy desktop computers that worked faster and cost less. Computers became more common in offices, schools, and homes.

↻ Many libraries have desktop computers for people to use.

A microchip ⟳

In 1981, Adam Osborne built a small computer that was also very light. It was called a **laptop**.

Laptops can do the same things that desktop computers can do. But people can use them in a smaller space. Laptops can weigh as little as three pounds. Since they are light, people can carry them from work, to home, to school. They can operate on batteries too. This means that people can use them when they travel.

↻ People often bring a laptop computer on board a train so they can work while they're traveling.

Word Workout

WORDS TO KNOW

dim   easily   farther   main

probably   solar system   telescope   temperatures

Hang On Choose one of the words and use it in a sentence. I'll choose another word and use it in a sentence that makes sense with yours. We'll keep trading, hanging sentences onto sentences.

SPELLING WORDS

throw   three   throne   thread   spree

spray   spread   screams   screens   scratch

scraped   scrubs   strong   stream   strength

"I Need More Letters Said thr, spr, scr, and str." Study the words for a minute or two. I'll give you a cluster of letters, such as **thr**. Try to remember the words with those letters and spell them aloud. Let's see how many you can remember.

© Macmillan/McGraw-Hill

(fold here)

Home-School Connection

Dear Family Member:

The Planets in Our Solar System gives us a big look at space and the planets in our universe. It tells us where and how Earth fits in. And it tells us interesting information about each of the planets. Did you know that the temperature on Venus is about 860 degrees? What I just told you is a summary of the book. It gives the main idea and one or two details about it. I'm looking forward to what else I'll learn.

This Week's Skills

Comprehension: summarize

Vocabulary: context clues

Spelling/Phonics: words with the letters **thr, spr, scr,** and **str**

Name _____

Pickin' Flowers

Let's read the article below.

A guide described the kinds of flowers we saw in our local garden. Bees love apple blossoms. Golden marigolds give off an odor that many insects do not like. Red and yellow rose petals are chopped and used in cooking. Just like people, flowers are special in their own ways.

We can use these clues to complete the puzzle. Then use the words to complete the summary.

1. most important
2. a thought
3. blossoms
4. red and long-stemmed
5. preparing food
6. turn away insects
7. exceptional, not usual

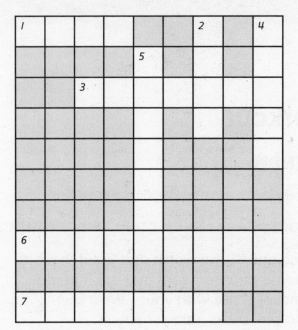

The 1 _____ 2 _____ is that there are many different types of

3 _____. They have different uses.

4 _____ are used in 5 _____.

And 6 _____ keep harmful insects away.

Each kind of flower is 7 _____, just like you and me.

Ejercicio de palabras

PALABRAS DE VOCABULARIO

dim   easily   farther   main

probably solar system telescope temperatures

Continuar oraciones Escoge una palabra y úsala en una oración. Yo escogeré otra palabra y la usaré en una oración vaya con la tuya. Seguiremos turnándonos para continuar una oración en otra oración.

PALABRAS DE ORTOGRAFÍA

throw   three   throne   thread   spree

spray   spread   screams   screens   scratch

scraped   scrubs   strong   stream   strength

thick   washing   whales   streamer   scribble

Necesito decir más letras thr, spr, scr, y str. Estudia las palabras por un minuto o dos. Te daré un grupo de letras, como por ejemplo thr. Trata de recordar todas las palabras que tengan esas letras y deletréalas en voz alta. Vamos a ver cuántas palabras puedes recordar.

(fold here)

Conexión con el hogar

Queridos familiares:

El libro titulado *The Planets in Our Solar System* nos ofrece una mirada general al espacio y los planetas en nuestro sistema solar. Nos dice dónde y cómo se encuentra el planeta Tierra. También nos ofrece información interesante acerca de cada uno de los planetas. ¿Sabías que la temperatura en Venus es de alrededor de 860 grados? Lo que te acabo de contar es un resumen del libro. Te dice cuál es la idea principal y uno o dos detalles sobre la misma. Quiero ver qué más voy a aprender.

Destrezas de la semana

Comprensión: resumir

Vocabulario: claves de contexto

Ortografía/Fonética: palabras con las letras **thr, spr, scr** y **str**

Nombre _____

Escogiendo flores

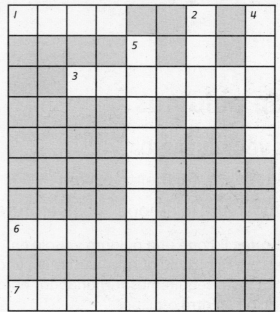

Leamos el artículo de abajo.

A guide described the kinds of flowers we saw in our local garden. Bees love apple blossoms. Golden marigolds give off an odor that many insects do not like. Red and yellow rose petals are chopped and used in cooking. Just like people, flowers are special in their own ways.

We can use these clues to complete the puzzle. Then use the words to complete the summary.

1. most important
2. a thought
3. blossoms
4. red and long-stemmed
5. preparing food
6. turns away insects
7. exceptional, not usual

The 1 _____ 2 _____ is that there are many different types of

3 _____. They have different uses.

4 _____ are used in 5 _____.

And 6 _____ keep harmful insects away.

Each kind of flower is 7 _____, just like you and me.

106

Comprehension Check

Summarize

Use a Main Idea Chart to record details and a main idea about the space station. Then use the chart to summarize what you learned from this book.

Main Idea	Details

Think and Compare

1. Reread pages 8 and 9. What other questions do you have about life on board the space station? *(Generate Questions)*

2. Would you like to be an astronaut one day? Why or why not? *(Synthesize)*

3. Why is it important to learn as much as possible about Earth and outer space? Explain your thinking. *(Evaluate)*

16

TheInternational Space Station

by Michael Teitelbaum

Table of Contents

Introduction

Have you ever wondered what it would be like to live in space? Scientists and astronauts are living in space right now. They live on board the International Space Station. They eat, drink, sleep, shower, and even brush their teeth 250 miles above Earth!

Why is the space station important? The space station is a science lab that orbits Earth. It is used to study the solar system. Scientists learn about the moon, the planets, and the **constellations**.

This is what the first International Space Station ⟳ looked like.

2

Glossary

constellation *(kon-stuh-LAY-shuhn)* stars in the sky that connect to form a picture *(page 2)*

dock *(DOK)* to bring two spacecraft together in space *(page 7)*

gravity *(GRAV-uh-tee)* the force that pulls things toward the center of Earth *(page 7)*

oxygen *(OK-si-juhn)* a colorless, tasteless gas that makes up part of the atmosphere *(page 12)*

simulator *(SIM-yuh-layt-uhr)* a machine that looks exactly like a real piece of equipment *(page 7)*

space shuttle *(SPAYS SHUT-uhl)* a spacecraft that carries a crew into space and returns to land on Earth *(page 7)*

weightless *(WAYT-les)* having little or no weight *(page 7)*

Index

15

Conclusion

In years to come, different astronauts will live aboard the space station. But their job will remain the same. They will continue to learn more about Earth and it's people.

Who knows? Maybe someday you will go through training, put on a space suit, and blast off for your new home among the stars!

↻ The International Space Station

The International Space Station

Chapter 1
A Home in Space

In 1971 the first space station was launched into orbit by the Soviet Union. It was called *Salyut*. It stayed in space only six months. In 1974, the United States launched a space station called *Skylab*. *Skylab* stayed in space until 1979.

In 1986 the Soviet Union put the space station *Mir* into orbit. It stayed in orbit for ten years.

Then, in 2000 a brand new space station called the International Space Station was ready.

It was the work of many nations. Its first crew began living and working there that same year.

Did You Know . . .

. . . that you can see the International Space Station when you visit the NASA Web site: http://spaceflight1.nasa.gov/realdata/sightings/cities/index.cgi

Each year new tools make the job of fixing the space station a bit easier. A new kind of radio lets up to five people talk at one time. Heaters help keep fingers warm. New lights on the space helmets shine on dim and dark work areas.

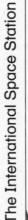

ROBOTIC ARM

One of the tools used by astronauts is the robotic arm. This large metal arm works like a giant space crane. It can move heavy equipment. It can also carry astronauts and place them outside of the station so they can make repairs.

Chapter 3
Making Repairs

When something breaks on the space station, what does the crew do? They fix it. To repair the outside of the space station they must take a space walk.

The temperature in space can be very hot or very cold. Astronauts wear space suits for protection. Their suits also provide air, since there is no **oxygen** in space.

What happens if gravity pulls astronauts away during a space walk? They use a jet-pack "life jacket" to easily fly back to the station.

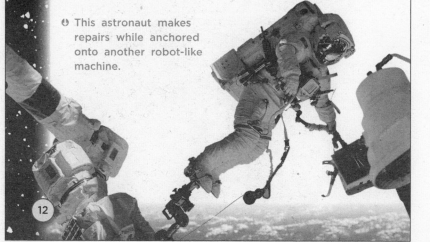

☝ This astronaut makes repairs while anchored onto another robot-like machine.

12

DREAMERS

In 1869, writer Edward Everett Hale wrote a story called "The Brick Moon." In this tale, a man-made structure orbits Earth to help ships at sea find their way. This is the first time the idea of a space station appeared in a book.

Space Stations

1986
The Soviet Union launches the *Mir* Space Station

1970 ———————————————— **2000**

1974
Skylab is launched into orbit.

2000
Crew members arrive at the International Space Station.

1971
Salyut is launched into orbit.

5

Astronauts go through years of schooling and training. Before living and working in space, they must complete a full year of even more training. They practice every part of their mission many times before ever leaving Earth.

This is a patch that will ↪ be used in future shuttle missions.

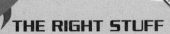

THE RIGHT STUFF

To be an astronaut, you must

- be healthy.
- have good eyesight.
- be between 64 and 76 inches tall.
- have had good grades.

© 2007 Macmillan/McGraw-Hill

Astronauts also study the brightness of stars. They take measurements to learn which stars are the farthest from Earth. They use telescopes to see stars close-up.

From space scientists study both Earth's weather and oceans. They can also take photos of the planet below.

GETTING ALONG

Astronauts on board the space station have to live together in a small space for six months. The crew has to solve problems and learn how to get along, just like family members do.

DREAMERS

In 1952 Dr. Werhner von Braun had the idea for an orbiting space station. The station would orbit more than 1,000 miles above Earth and spin to create its own gravity.

More than anything else, the main mission of the space station is to learn.

Scientists want to learn how our planet was formed. They want to learn more about earthquakes. They are also trying to learn more about how our bodies work. They are trying to find cures for some diseases.

Did You Know . . .

A light-year is the distance you would travel if you moved at the speed of light (186,000 miles each second) for one year.

The crew uses machines called **simulators**. These machines look and act just like the equipment that is on the **space shuttle** and on the space station. The crew uses them to learn how to pilot the space shuttle. They learn how to **dock** the space shuttle to the space station.

⊕ This astronaut is working in a simulator.

Space has no **gravity**, so everything in space is **weightless**. Astronauts need to learn what it is like to be weightless. To do this, they wear special suits.

↻ Astronauts practice walking on the botton of a large tank of water.

Chapter 2
On Board

What do astronauts do on board the space station? In many ways, their days can be compared to yours.

Crew members eat breakfast, lunch, and dinner. Some food is dry. To eat it, the crew adds water. Some food has been heated, then stored in cans. Some food is simply sealed in foil packs. Then the crew warms it in ovens on the space station.

Crew members wash their clothes in plastic bags filled with soap and water. Then they squeeze the clothes with their hands. They wrap the clothes in towels to dry.

🪐 Menu 🪐

BREAKFAST:
Granola with Raisins
Breakfast Roll
Pears
Vanilla Breakfast Drink

LUNCH:
Chicken Strips in Salsa
Macaroni & Cheese
Rice with Butter
Apple Cider

DINNER:
Shrimp Cocktail
Beef Steak
Fruit Cocktail
Strawberry Drink

🎧 Astronauts get mail in space. They are trying to organize it here.

The crew uses a special shampoo to wash their hair. You probably think they use water, but they don't. They just comb the shampoo through their hair.

There are no beds in space. Crew members sleep in sleeping bags which are attached to a wall. This keeps them from floating away!

Did You Know . . .
The space station has as much room inside as a jumbo jet.

Word Workout

WORDS TO KNOW

acceptance	excitement	proper
single	talented	useful

Word Search Let's talk about what these words mean. Then tell me about a book or an article you have read lately. We can use some of the words in the list to talk about the book and what the author wanted to tell us.

SPELLING WORDS

wrong	wrap	wrists	wrote
knock	know	knight	knit
knots	sign	gnat	gnaws
write	wreck	wring	

I Can't Hear You! I'm going to list all the words leaving out the letter you can't hear. For example, for *wrong* I'd write *rong*. Can you fill in the silent letter? Can you think of other words you've learned that have a silent letter?

© Macmillan/McGraw-Hill

(fold here)

Home-School Connection

Dear Family Member:

An author usually has a reason for writing each book he or she writes. The story I'm reading this week is *Author, A True Story*. I laugh as Helen Lester tells us about everything she learned about writing from the time she was three to when she is a grownup. This is a very funny book, but the author also tells us how she had a dream and just kept trying and trying to reach it. So, she's got two reasons for writing this book—to give us a good time and to tell us not to give up.

This Week's Skills

Comprehension: author's purpose

Vocabulary: context clues

Spelling/Phonics: silent letters in words with **kn, wr,** and **gn**

Name _____

Writing Reasons

Look at the picture clues to help you understand why the author is writing each item. Let's talk about each reason. We can also make up additions to each item.

Ejercicio de palabras

PALABRAS DE VOCABULARIO

acceptance	excitement	proper
single	talented	useful

Búsqueda de palabras Hablemos acerca de lo que estas palabras significan. Luego dime un libro o un artículo que hayas leído últimamente. Podemos usar algunas de las palabras en la lista para hablar acerca del libro y sobre lo que el autor o autora nos quiere decir.

PALABRAS DE ORTOGRAFÍA

wrong	wrap	wrists	wrote
knock	know	knight	knit
knots	sign	gnat	gnaws
write	wreck	wring	

¡No te escucho! Voy a escribir todas las palabras sin poner la letra que no puedes escuchar. Por ejemplo, para la palabra *wrong* escribiré *rong*. ¿Puedes completar la palabra con la letra muda que falta? ¿Puedes pensar de otras palabras que has aprendido que tienen una letra muda?

(fold here)

© Macmillan/McGraw-Hill

Conexión con el hogar

Queridos familiares:

En general, un autor tiene un motivo para escribir cada libro. El relato que estoy leyendo esta semana se llama *Author, A True Story*. Me río cuando Helen Lester nos cuenta acerca de todo lo que ella aprendió sobre escritura desde que tenía tres años de edad hasta su edad adulta. Este libro es muy divertido, pero la autora también nos cuenta cómo ella tenía un sueño y seguía tratando de conseguirlo. Ella tiene dos motivos para escribir este libro: hacernos pasar un buen rato y decirnos que no nos demos por vencidos.

Destrezas de la semana

Comprensión: propósito del autor

Vocabulario: claves de contexto

Ortografía/Fonética: las letras mudas en palabras con **kn, wr** y **gn**

Nombre_____

Motivos

Observa los dibujos para buscar pistas sobre para escribir
por qué el autor o la autora está escribiendo cada artículo.
Hablemos acerca de cada motivo. También podemos agregar
cosas a cada artículo.

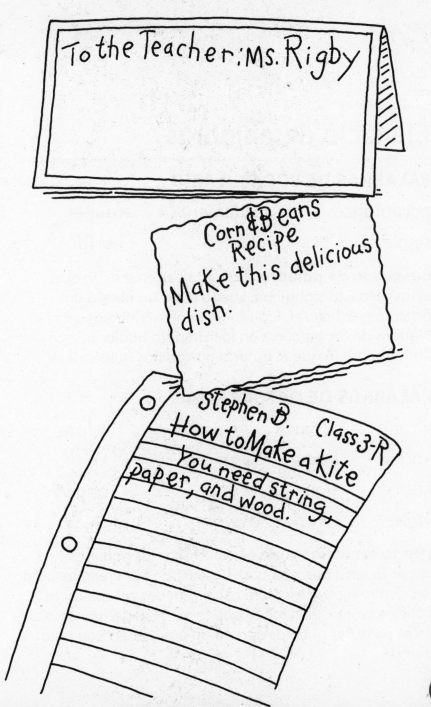

Comprehension Check

Summarize

Use an Author's Purpose Chart to tell about E.B. White's life. Use the information to record clues about why the author wrote this book. Then summarize the book.

Clues

↓

Author's Purpose

Think and Compare

1. Reread page 13. Explain why E.B. White decided to write for children. *(Evaluate Author's Purpose)*

2. What about E.B. White's life did you find most interesting? Explain. *(Apply)*

3. Some authors seem to know what children like to read more than others. Who are some popular authors? Why are they popular? *(Synthesize)*

E.B. White, Writer

by Justine Fontes

Table of Contents

Introduction

E.B. White was a talented writer. He could make readers laugh and cry. White's children's books are about the things he loved. His writings helped readers see these things through his eyes. When he wrote, he described what it felt like to be a mouse, a spider, or a swan.

In his first book, *Stuart Little*, a mouse sails, drives, and looks for love. *Charlotte's Web* tells of a doomed piglet and a smart spider who become friends. A mute swan learns to express himself in *The Trumpet of the Swan*.

> **" This is the finest thing I have ever done! "**
> —*Stuart Little*

© 2007 Macmillan/McGraw-Hill

E.B. White, Writer

Glossary

classic *(KLA-sik)* a book that is so good people enjoy it for years *(page 13)*

editor-in-chief *(Ed-i-tuhr IN CHEEF)* the person who decides what gets published *(page 10)*

publisher *(PU-bli-shuhr)* a company that prints and sells books *(page 13)*

Pulitzer Prize *(PU-luht-suhr PRIGHZ)* an award given every year for outstanding writing *(page 14)*

Index

© 2007 Macmillan/McGraw-Hill

Conclusion

In 1978, E.B. White won the **Pulitzer Prize** for his writing.

White never lost a child's joy in little things. He liked watching eggs hatch. He liked to watch the sunset. And he even liked a blank sheet of paper. He knew he could fill it with stories that people would enjoy.

E.B. White's Children's Books

1945 STUART LITTLE

1952 CHARLOTTE'S WEB

1970 THE TRUMPET OF THE SWAN

14

3

CHAPTER 1 **Family Life**

Elwyn Brooks White was born on July 11, 1899. He was the baby in his family. He had three sisters and two brothers. His brother, Stanley, taught him to read before he even started school.

⌐ White is the youngest child in this family picture.

© 2007 Macmillan/McGraw-Hill

E.B. White, Writer

White often told stories to his nieces and nephews. Their favorite stories were about a well-dressed mouse. So White put these stories in a book. After many drafts, *Stuart Little* finally found acceptance from a **publisher** who agreed to print it.

Readers loved the book and wanted more. So White wrote *Charlotte's Web* and *The Trumpet of the Swan*. These became **classics**, as well.

White is also famous for a useful book he wrote for adults about the proper way to write.

⌐ White saw trumpeter swans when he took a trip to the western part of the United States.

Book Sales

All three of E.B. White's children's books are bestsellers. In its first 30 years in print, *Stuart Little* sold over 2 ½ million copies. Both *Charlotte's Web* and *The Trumpet of the Swan* each sold over 6 million copies during their first 30 years in print. All three books are still read all over the world.

White worked at *The New Yorker* for many years. White liked the excitement of city life, but he decided to give up his full-time job. He moved from New York City to a farm in Maine. He wanted to be that single loon at dawn. He wanted to explore the misty ponds once again.

> 66 When the first light comes into the sky and the sparrows stir ... I will show you my masterpiece. 99
>
> —*Charlotte's Web*

© 2007 Macmillan/McGraw-Hill

> 66 I'm not tall enough to be noticed ... yet I'm tall enough to want to go to Seventy-second Street. 99
>
> —*Stuart Little*

All six White children learned music. After dinner, the Whites played music together.

They also did their homework. Mr. and Mrs. White had been too poor to stay in school. But they wanted their children to get a good education.

> 66 Bother arithmetic! Let's skip it. 99
>
> —*Stuart Little*

The Whites lived in Mount Vernon, a city near New York City. Mount Vernon was more like a rural town in those days. A boy could still find many wild animals. White always had a dog and lots of other pets. He kept birds, bunnies, lizards, snakes, and mice.

Did you Know?

During White's childhood, people traveled mostly by horse and carriage, and by train. Many families kept horses. White loved to spend time in the stables behind his home.

◐ The Whites lived in a comfortable house in Mount Vernon, NY.

E.B. White, Writer

◠ This is Cornell University where White studied.

Katharine Angell, an editor, read it and laughed out loud. She told her boss to hire White.

White and Angell married in 1929. A year later, their only child, Joel, was born.

66 It was just a cheap notebook that was always by his bed. Every night he wrote about things he had done, things he had seen, and thoughts he had had. 99

—*The Trumpet of the Swan*

© 2007 Macmillan/McGraw-Hill

E.B. White, Writer

CHAPTER 3 Becoming a Writer

At the age of eight, White started writing a journal. He wrote letters to his brothers at college. He wrote poems and stories. Many of them were about animals. White's poem about a mouse won a prize from a magazine called *Woman's Home Companion*.

Then White went to college. He soon was named **editor-in-chief** of the school newspaper. Readers loved the way White made fun of the news. White also became friends with other writers.

In 1925, White sent a funny story to a new magazine called *The New Yorker*.

> ❝ It is not often that someone comes along who is a true friend and a good writer. Charlotte was both. ❞
> —*Charlotte's Web*

CHAPTER 2 Animals All Around

White loved all of nature's beginnings, like birds hatching and the sun rising on a new day. One day, Mr. White brought home a crate of chicken eggs. Elwyn was excited when the first chick pecked free of its shell. He spent many fun hours watching the eggs hatch.

⊙ White once built a gym for a mouse and trained it to do tricks.

> ❝ I don't know of anything in the entire world more wonderful to look at than a nest with eggs in it. ❞
> —*The Trumpet of the Swan*

White loved nature. But nature did not always love him. Six-year-old Elwyn came down with hay fever. Mr. White thought living in the country might help. So the family went to Maine for the summers.

> 66 ... summers are wonderful, aren't they... ? 99
>
> —*Stuart Little*

⟲ Pine Island, Belgrade Lakes, Maine

© 2007 Macmillan/McGraw-Hill

E.B. White, Writer

⟲ White loved exploring the Maine lakes with his brother Stanley.

White fell in love with Maine's wildlife. He loved Great Pond, one of the lakes there.

He would wake up early to explore. At dawn, he might spot a single loon in the mist. Then he would watch it flap above the water and fly into the sky. At times he felt like he was flying too.

> 66 ... my canoe is like an old and trusted friend. 99
>
> —*Stuart Little*

Word Workout

WORDS TO KNOW

agreeable   banquet   curiosity

gaze   guests   untrusting

Fit for a King Let's use the words to make up a story about the night a king gave an amazing feast.

SPELLING WORDS

hard	sport	bark	sharp
sharks	carve	yard	storms
shorts	sore	wore	pour
story	chore	porch	

Words Plus We can practice your spelling words, and then think of more words with **ar** and **or** that you've learned.

Home-School Connection

Dear Family Member:

In *Stone Soup* three monks are traveling, and they find a village in which the people are very hungry. The monks decide to show the villagers how to make soup out of stones. One by one, people bring things to put in the soup. I can make an inference. I think the monks are showing the people how to make soup together.

This Week's Skills

Comprehension: make inferences

Vocabulary: synonyms

Spelling/Phonics: words with **ar** and **or**

Name _____

Coming Attractions

Let's look at the pictures and talk about them. We can think about how to answer the questions and tell each other why we answered the way we did.

What kind of boy is Mario?

What is the boy feeling? What does he expect?

Will Rosita's running practice pay off?

What kind of boy is Hakim?

Ejercicio de palabras

PALABRAS DE VOCABULARIO

agreeable	banquet	curiosity
gaze	guests	untrusting

A la medida de un rey Usemos las palabras para escribir un cuento acerca de la noche en la que un rey ofreció un banquete increíble.

PALABRAS DE ORTOGRAFÍA

hard	sport	bark	sharp
sharks	carve	yard	storms
shorts	sore	wore	pour
story	chore	porch	

Palabras adicionales Podemos practicar tus palabras de ortografía y luego pensar en más palabras con **ar** y **or** que has aprendido.

Conexión con el hogar

Queridos familiares:

En *Stone Soup* tres monjes están viajando y llegan a un pueblo en el que la gente está muy hambrienta. Los monjes deciden mostrarles a los habitantes del pueblo cómo hacer sopa con piedras. Cada persona lleva cosas para poner en la sopa. Puedo hacer una inferencia. Pienso que los monjes están mostrándole a la gente cómo preparar sopa todos juntos.

Destrezas de la semana

Comprensión: hacer inferencias

Vocabulario: sinónimos

Ortografía/Fonética: palabras con **ar** y **or**

Nombre _____

Próximas atracciones

Observemos los dibujos y hablemos acerca de ellos. Podemos pensar cómo responder a las preguntas y decirnos por qué respondimos de la manera en que lo hicimos.

What kind of boy is Mario?

What is the boy feeling?
What does he expect?

Will Rosita's running practice pay off?

What kind of boy is Hakim?

Comprehension Check

Summarize the Story

Complete an Inference Map to record clues and make inferences about how the fox behaved. Then use the map to help summarize the story.

Clue
↓
Clue
↓
Clue
↓
Inference

Think and Compare

1. Turn to page 3. Why is Earth so drab looking? *(Make Inferences)*

2. Think of a time that you were nervous about meeting someone new or being a guest in a new place. Explain how you felt before and after the experience. *(Apply)*

3. Why do you think people write stories about where plants and animals came from? *(Analyze)*

The Fox's Banquet

by Susan Blackaby
illustrated by Barbara Spurll

Table of Contents

Chapter 1
A Visitor

A long time ago, only a few plants grew on Earth. Hungry animals roamed everywhere, looking for food. Everyone was always hungry.

One morning a little fox worked his way up to a flat place at the top of a mountain bluff. From his high perch, the fox could see for miles and miles. The drab world stretched from the mountains to the sea. Looking down at it made the fox feel gloomy and lonely.

© 2007 Macmillan/McGraw-Hill

Where there had been bare ground, plants grew. Vines, trees, and bushes popped up everywhere. A green carpet spread out in every direction. For the first time, leaves sprouted on new branches. Buds blossomed and flowers bloomed. Fruit turned from green to red, yellow, pink, and orange. The gray, dull Earth turned into a beautiful blue and green jewel.

The fox walked around smelling the flowers and tasting the sweet green leaves and all the delicious fruits and vegetables.

Then one bright fall day, the fox went to the top of the mountain to welcome the birds to Earth's wonderful feast.

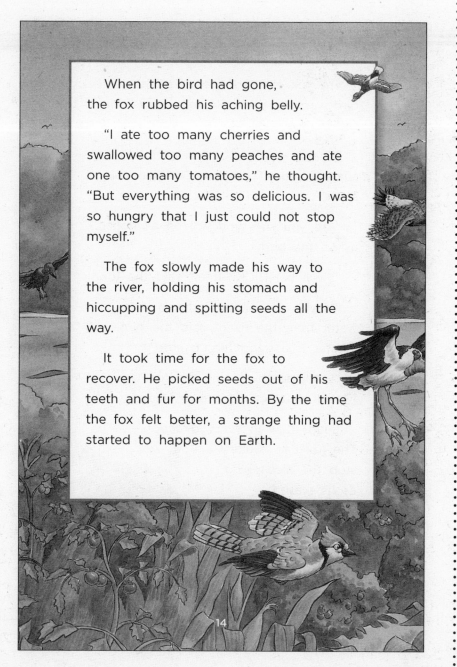

When the bird had gone, the fox rubbed his aching belly.

"I ate too many cherries and swallowed too many peaches and ate one too many tomatoes," he thought. "But everything was so delicious. I was so hungry that I just could not stop myself."

The fox slowly made his way to the river, holding his stomach and hiccupping and spitting seeds all the way.

It took time for the fox to recover. He picked seeds out of his teeth and fur for months. By the time the fox felt better, a strange thing had started to happen on Earth.

14

The Fox's Banquet

3

The fox turned his gaze upward, toward the deep blue sky. He liked to watch the birds that lived up in the clouds. The birds chirped and chattered and flapped their bright wings. The fox loved to look at them spinning and twirling in the air.

"I wish I could fly like that," he thought. "Where do those birds get all their energy? They must have a secret. There must be plenty to eat up there in those puffy clouds."

4

The fox climbed down from the bird's aching back. He felt dizzy from the bumpy trip.

"Thank —HICK! you!" said the fox, spitting seeds. "I will—HICK!—see you soon."

"Are you sure you will be all right?" asked the bird.

"I will be—HICK!—fine," said the fox.

"Maybe you should drink a little water from the river," said the bird. "Water is a good hiccup cure."

"I will do that," said the fox. "Thank you again for everything."

Seeds flew in every direction. The fox just couldn't stop the hiccupping as he waved goodbye.

13

Chapter 4
A Brand New World

"I'm feeling extremely woozy," said the fox. He wiggled around, trying to get comfortable.

"Maybe you ate too much," said the bird.

The fox bubbled and burped and moaned and groaned.

HICK! The fox spit out a mouthful of seeds.

"Excuse me," said the fox, "I have the hiccups."

HICK! The fox spit out another mouthful of seeds.

The bird bucked and rocked with each hick. At last they reached the mountaintop, and the bird skidded in for a landing.

© 2007 Macmillan/McGraw-Hill

Day after day, the fox searched for food. Day after day, he climbed up the mountain to watch the birds.

One day the fox was sitting in his usual place when some birds came twittering and fluttering overhead.

Suddenly a dark shadow blocked his view. At first the fox thought that rain clouds must be blowing in from the ocean. But it was not a storm. It was a huge bird with wings that seemed to fill the sky. The bird circled over the fox's head as it glided down from a cloud.

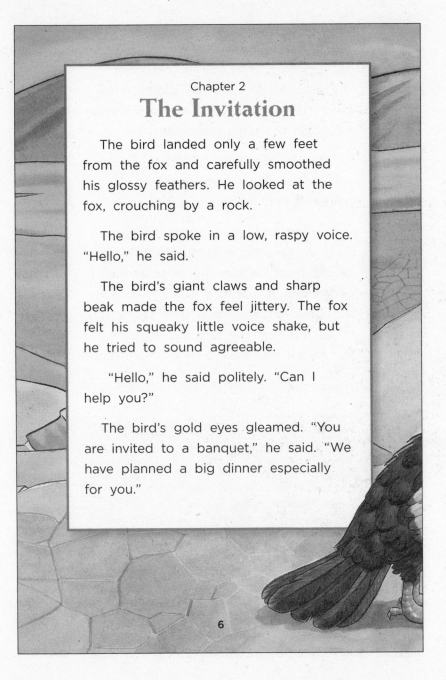

© 2007 Macmillan/McGraw-Hill

Chapter 2
The Invitation

The bird landed only a few feet from the fox and carefully smoothed his glossy feathers. He looked at the fox, crouching by a rock.

The bird spoke in a low, raspy voice. "Hello," he said.

The bird's giant claws and sharp beak made the fox feel jittery. The fox felt his squeaky little voice shake, but he tried to sound agreeable.

"Hello," he said politely. "Can I help you?"

The bird's gold eyes gleamed. "You are invited to a banquet," he said. "We have planned a big dinner especially for you."

"The banquet was delicious," said the fox.

The fox waddled over to the big bird. His tummy was as round as a big, ripe watermelon. Two sea gulls helped boost him up onto the bird's back.

The bird glided down toward the brown, dusty Earth. They had not gone very far before the fox began to feel queasy.

"Please pass the peas," said the fox. "Please pass the berries and cherries."

The fox filled his mouth again and again. He did not even stop long enough to spit out the pits and seeds. He just swallowed and stuffed and swallowed and stuffed. Everyone ate until there was not a speck of food left.

When it was time to go home, the fox gratefully thanked the birds.

10

© 2007 Macmillan/McGraw-Hill

The Fox's Banquet

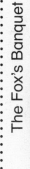

"For me?" said the fox. "Why?" The fox did not mean to sound untrusting, but he wanted to be sure that the bird wasn't trying to trick him.

"We see you every day, you poor little thing," said the bird. "We know how hungry you must be."

"That is true," said the fox sadly.

"We see you pawing at the dirt, so we want to treat you to a special meal," said the bird. "Come on, hop onto my back."

7

Chapter 3
The Party

The fox climbed onto the big bird's back and held on tightly. The bird hopped and scuttled to the edge of the bluff, flapping his big wings.

Soon other birds flew out to meet them. Geese and storks flapped alongside the big bird. Robins, flickers, crows, and jays darted to and fro. All of the birds chirped their greetings to the fox.

Finally the big bird landed in a large hall deep in the clouds. The fox slid off the bird's back and looked around. He was filled with curiosity about this wonderful place.

In the middle of the hall stretched a long, wide table. It was loaded with plates and platters piled high with food. The fox could not believe what he was seeing.

8

© 2007 Macmillan/McGraw-Hill

"Help yourself," said a bright blue jay. "Guests and visitors always go first."

The fox began to fill up his plate. He ate peaches, plums, beans, peppers, squash, and corn. He ate olives, tomatoes, apples, and oranges. He stuffed his cheeks with grapes and mangoes.

While the fox gobbled and chomped, the birds pecked at the nutritious fruits and vegetables. They supped and sipped.

9

Word Workout

WORDS TO KNOW

advised   depart   discouraged   increase

observed   suitable   wearily

At the Airport Let's make up a story about travelers at an airport waiting for their flights to take off.

SPELLING WORDS

mare	dares	glare	stairs	their
hare	bear	wear	chairs	square
pears	pairs	share	bare	haircut

Three-Way Street There are four spelling patterns here. Words with **are, air, eir,** and **ear.** I'll give you a word, and you tell me which pattern is in the word. Then spell the word. Would you like to test me?

Home-School Connection

Dear Family Member:

In *One Riddle, One Answer*, a sultan wants to find a husband for his daughter, Aziza. She makes up a riddle and vows to marry only the man who can come up with the answer. She travels across the land to different settings, but no one can solve the puzzle. I think that the plot will end with Aziza finding a man to marry.

This Week's Skills

Comprehension: plot and setting

Vocabulary: use a dictionary

Spelling/Phonics: words with **are, air, eir,** and **ear**

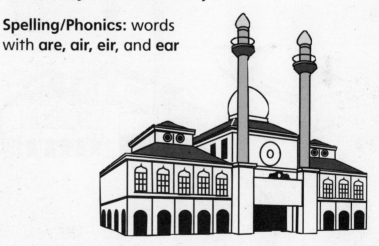

Name _____

(fold here)

It's Your Story

We can make up a story. Here's how we'll do it.

• Let's look at the pictures of settings and circle the one we like best.
• Let's talk about what each of the characters might be like and choose one or more for our story.
• Then we can write what happens in the beginning, middle, and end of our story.

Characters

Kaneesha   Tony   Mr. Ruiz

   Taffy, the dog   Captain Pete

Setting

Beginning

Middle

End

Ejercicio de palabras

PALABRAS DE VOCABULARIO

advised	depart	discouraged	increase
observed	suitable	wearily	

En el aeropuerto Inventemos un cuento sobre unos viajeros en un aeropuerto mientras esperan que sus aviones despeguen.

PALABRAS DE ORTOGRAFÍA

mare	dares	glare	stairs	their
hare	bear	wear	chairs	square
pears	pairs	share	bare	haircut

Calle de tres vías Aquí tenemos cuatros patrones de ortografía: palabras con **are, air, eir** y **ear.** Te voy a dar una palabra y tú me dirás qué patrón aparece en la palabra. Luego, deletrea la palabra. ¿Te gustaría tomarme una prueba?

·(fold here)·

Conexión con el hogar

Queridos familiares:

En *One Riddle, One Answer*, un sultán quiere encontrar un esposo para su hija. Aziza inventa una adivinanza y sólo se va a casar con el hombre que pueda responderla. Aziza viaja por diferentes lugares, pero nadie puede resolver la adivinanza. Pienso que el argumento va a terminar con Aziza encontrando a un hombre para casarse.

Destrezas de la semana

Comprensión: argumento y ambiente

Vocabulario: usar un diccionario

Ortografía/Fonética: palabras con **are, air, eir** y **ear**

Nombre_____

Es tu cuento

Vamos a escribir un cuento. Leamos a cómo hacerlo:
- Imaginemos cada uno de los ambientes y encerremos en un círculo el que nos guste más.
- Hablemos acerca de cómo podría ser cada personaje y escojamos uno o más para nuestro cuento.
- Luego, podemos escribir lo que ocurre en el comienzo, en el medio y en el final de nuestro cuento.

Characters

Kaneesha   Tony   Mr. Ruiz

    Taffy, the dog   Captain Pete

Setting

Beginning

Middle

End

Comprehension Check

Summarize

Use a Setting Web to tell where the story takes place. Then summarize the story, describing the action in each setting.

Think and Compare

1. Look back at pages 2–3. How did living on a farm affect the brothers' lives? *(Analyze Plot and Setting)*

2. Make up your own math riddle. Exchange your riddle with a classmate's. Solve it. *(Synthesize)*

3. How will knowing math help you in the real world? Give some examples. *(Apply)*

16

Magpie's Mystery

by Suzanne Weyn
illustrated by Trevor Howard

Table of Contents

Chapter 1 **A Strange Bird**

Once, long ago in Mexico, three brothers lived on a small farm. The soil was rocky. There was not much rain. Their crops did not grow well. For these reasons, they were very poor.

Each day Pablo the youngest brother got up before sunrise. Then he crept silently out of the house while his brothers, Manuel and Juan, snored. Pablo walked many miles to the nearest school.

He couldn't spend the whole day at school because he had to return home to help his brothers on the farm.

So the three brothers returned home. Every morning, they rose before dawn to walk to school. Before long, Juan and Manuel found that they liked school too.

The brothers grew smart. They spent their fortune wisely. They kept going to school and—thanks to the magpie's nest of treasure—they were able to go in style.

"Here comes Mr. Smart Guy," Manuel would tease Pablo when he returned. Manuel had never gone to school and he didn't want to go. He didn't understand why Pablo liked it so much.

"You should spend more time working and less time learning," Juan would advise Pablo. He, too, thought school didn't matter.

"Learning is important," Pablo would answer. "Someday it will pay off. You'll see." Then wearily he would start plowing the rocky soil.

Every day the brothers observed a black and white bird flying over their field. It was a magpie, and it was always carrying something. The brothers knew that magpies loved to collect shiny objects. And the birds often hid what they found in their nests.

Their curiosity began to increase each day as they watched the bird. Where was it going? What was it carrying?

One day on his way home from school Pablo met his brothers on the road. "Where are you going?" Pablo asked.

"We are following the magpie. We want to find the treasure it keeps in its nest," they told him. "Come, we will share the riches we find."

Pablo and his brothers traveled many miles. Finally, they came to a group of very tall trees.

© 2007 Macmillan/McGraw-Hill

Manuel and Juan shouted happily, "We're rich! We're rich." They tried to grab the treasure.

Pablo held on tight to the nest. "Not so fast," he said. "I won this treasure because I learned the answer to the magpie's riddle in school. Before I share this fortune, you two must go to school."

"School?" Juan and Manuel cried.

"Yes," Pablo told them. "We should respect the magpie's wise words. We must learn how to spend this fortune wisely."

Chapter 3 Pablo's Deal

"How clever you are," the magpie said.

Pablo disagreed. "Not really. I simply listen in school, and I knew some day it would pay off."

The magpie carried its nest to the ground. Pablo climbed down the tree where Juan was waiting for him. "Where is Manuel?" Pablo asked the magpie. "Is he safe?"

"You have answered for your entire family so I will bring your brother back," the magpie said.

It flew off and soon returned with Manuel. "Spend the treasure wisely," the magpie advised. "Now I must depart. Goodbye." In a flash, the bird was gone.

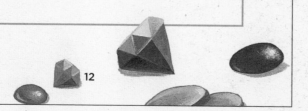

12

They heard a loud bird call—*chaw-chaw-chaw-chaw-chaw*. "That sounds like a magpie," Pablo said.

"It's up there!" Manuel observed, pointing.

There, indeed, sat the magpie on its large nest of mud and sticks. It was messy but perfectly suitable for a magpie. Something in the nest sparkled.

"Its nest is filled with treasure!" Juan cried. "Let's get it!" So the three brothers began to climb up the tree.

5

The brothers had almost reached the nest when a voice shouted, "Stop!" They looked in every direction. Who had spoken? "Why are you here? What do you want?" the voice spoke again. They then realized it was the magpie speaking to them.

The brothers knew right away that this was a special bird. "We were hoping you would give us your shiny things," Manuel said. "Those things would help us a great deal."

6

"For example, in the number 34 the digits three plus four equal seven. But three is not three less than four."

"My brother made one mistake. In his answer the digit in the tens place is three more than the digit in the ones place. Not three less."

11

Pablo watched as the magpie shrunk to its normal size. Pablo tried to remember what he had learned in his math class. "I think I know," he said. "The answer to your riddle is 25!"

The magpie gasped. "That's right! How did you know?"

"There are many ways to add digits to reach the sum of seven," Pablo explained.

"Six plus one makes seven. So does three plus four."

"Go on," said the magpie.

"Five plus two equals seven. So does two plus five. But it is only in the number 25 that the digit in the tens place is three less than the digit in the digit in the ones place.

© 2007 Macmillan/McGraw-Hill

Magpie's Mystery

"That may be true," the magpie said, "but finding treasure has been my life's work. Every day I pick up some jewelry or a coin that someone has dropped. It has taken me a lifetime to collect this fortune. I will not give it to fools."

"We're not fools," Pablo said.

The magpie replied, "I will test you. Answer my riddle and I will give you my treasure. If you cannot, I will fly you across the land and drop you in some strange place."

"Let's hear this riddle," Manuel said. "We are smart so this will not be difficult for us."

Chapter 2 **Solving the Riddle**

"Here it is," the magpie said with a sly look. "Listen carefully."

The magpie flew to a branch near the brothers and spoke. "I am a two-digit number. The sum of my digits is seven. The digit in my tens place is three less than the digit in my ones place. What number am I?"

The brothers thought and thought. The riddle was harder than they had expected.

After awhile Juan cried, "I've got it! The number 52. The sum of five and two is seven. And two is three less than five."

"Wrong!" the magpie cried. "Wrong!" The bird seemed to grow much, much larger.

It scooped up the shocked Manuel by his shirt and flew away with him.

Pablo and Juan were frightened. They didn't want to be carried through the sky by a bird.

Juan became discouraged. "I give up!" he shouted. Juan tried to grab for the nest. He was about to pull it down, when the large magpie returned. Juan was so startled that he fell straight down to the ground.

Word Workout

WORDS TO KNOW

preserve   rainfall   restore   suffered

Save the Environment Let's talk about how each of the words can be used in telling something about our environment.

SPELLING WORDS

firm	first	third	perch	world
learn	turns	word	purr	girls
worth	nurse	earn	serve	herds

Before the R Look for the letters **er, ir, ear, or,** and **ur** in your spelling words. Then I'll give you a word to spell. Tell me which letter pattern is in the word and spell the word for me.

(fold here)

Home-School Connection

Dear Family Member:

Sand dunes protect beaches, but big storms can make the dunes disappear. In "Saving the Sand Dunes," we're reading how the kids in a fourth-grade class built a special wall for the sand dunes. They took old Christmas trees and buried them in the dunes. The storms ruin the dunes, so the kids built a wall, and I wonder what will happen next. I see how one thing makes something else happen.

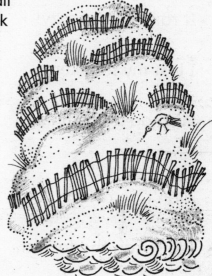

This Week's Skills

Comprehension: cause and effect

Vocabulary: multiple-meaning words

Spelling/Phonics: words with **er, ir, ear, or,** and **ur**

Name _____

Why Did That Happen?

Let's read the different causes and effects below and talk about them. Then we can match them up.

Cause	Effect
It rained like crazy!	I was nervous.
I lost my sneakers.	I kept on sleeping.
We had a pop quiz.	Her team won.
The alarm clock didn't go off!	We didn't have recess.
Claire ran the fastest.	I went barefoot.

Why? Because! Why?

Riddles can also show cause and effect!
Let's ask family members and friends to solve these riddles.

Q: What kind of television does a zebra watch?

A: _____ and _____.

Q: Why can't you believe what a balloon says?

A: Because it's full of _____.

Q: Why do kids go to school in autumn through spring?

A: So they can have summer _____.

Q: Why do seagulls live near the sea?

A: If they lived near a bay, they'd be called _____.

Q: What time is it when an elephant sits on a fence?

A: Time to build a new _____.

Ejercicio de palabras

PALABRAS DE VOCABULARIO

preserve   rainfall   restore   suffered

Salvar el medio ambiente Hablemos sobre cómo cada una de las palabras puede ser usada para contar algo acerca de nuestro medio ambiente.

PALABRAS DE ORTOGRAFÍA

firm   first   third   perch   world

learn   turns   word   purr   girls

worth   nurse   earn   serve   herds

Antes de la R Busca las letras **er, ir, ear, or** y **ur** en tus palabras de ortografía. Luego te voy a dar una palabra para deletrear. Dime qué grupo de letras hay en la palabra y deletréamela.

(fold here)

© Macmillan/McGraw-Hill

Conexión con el hogar

Queridos familiares:

Las dunas de arena protegen las playas, pero las grandes tormentas pueden hacer que las dunas desaparezcan. En *Saving the Sand Dunes*, estamos leyendo cómo una clase de cuarto grado construyó una pared especial para las dunas de arena. Enterraron árboles de Navidad en las dunas. Como las tormentas destruyen las dunas, entonces los niños construyeron una pared. Me pregunto qué va a ocurrir después. Veo cómo una cosa hace que ocurra otra cosa.

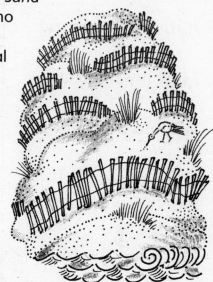

Destrezas de la semana

Comprensión: causa y efecto

Voacabulario: palabras con múltiple significado

Ortografía/Fonética: palabras con **er, ir, ear, or** y **ur**

Nombre_____

¿Por qué ocurrió eso?

Leamos las causas y los efectos a continuación y hablemos acerca de ellos. Luego, podemos emparejarlos.

Cause	Effect
It rained like crazy!	I was nervous.
I lost my sneakers.	I kept on sleeping.
We had a pop quiz.	Her team won.
The alarm clock didn't go off!	We didn't have recess.
Claire ran the fastest.	I went barefoot.

¿Por qué? ¡Por eso!

¡Las adivinanzas también pueden describir causas y efectos! Pidamos a nuestros familiares y amigos que resuelvan éstas.

Q: What kind of television does a zebra watch?

A: _____ and _____.

Q: Why can't you believe what a balloon says?

A: Because it's full of _____.

Q: Why do kids go to school in autumn through spring?

A: So they can have summer _____.

Q: Why do seagulls live near the sea?

A: If they lived near a bay, they'd be called _____.

Q: What time is it when an elephant sits on a fence?

A: Time to build a new _____.

Comprehension Check

Summarize

Use the photographs in this book to tell what is happening to our deserts. Then summarize what you learned from this book.

Think and Compare

1. Reread pages 12-13. Why is it important to preserve our deserts? *(Identify Cause and Effect)*

2. What part of this book did you enjoy the most? What other things would you like to know about the desert? Where can you find more information about it? *(Synthesize)*

3. More and more people are moving into or near our deserts. To live in a desert, people need water. How might bringing more water to the desert affect plants and animals? *(Evaluate)*

Water in the Desert

by Sheila Black

Table of Contents

Introduction

They cover one-seventh of Earth. They can be sandy or rocky. They all have one thing in common. They are hot and dry. They are the world's deserts.

Some deserts are formed when winds blow warm air that dries out the land. Other deserts form when tall mountains prevent moisture from reaching land on the other side.

This is part of the ↻ Sonoran Desert.

All of the deserts in ↻ the United States are in the Southwest or West.

2

Glossary

absorb *(ab-ZAWRB)* to soak up or take in *(page 7)*

adapt *(uh-DAPT)* to make or become used to *(page 5)*

environment *(en-VIGH-ruhn-muhnt)* the air, the water, the soil, and other things that surround a person, animal, or plant *(page 14)*

evaporate *(i-VAP-uh-rayt)* to change into a vapor or gas *(page 10)*

survive *(suhr-VIGHV)* to live through *(page 5)*

Index

15

Conclusion

Living in the desert **environment** is harsh. But the plants and animals that live there have adapted. They survive with little water and make good use of the rains.

Desert plants and animals may die out, however, if too many people move into the deserts. People have to learn how to preserve and restore our deserts. They need to save its water too.

↻ This young girl is hiking in the Superstition Mountains area of Arizona.

↻ This lake covers desert land in Arizona and Utah. It was created by the Glen Canyon Dam.

Although deserts are mainly dry, there are lakes in some parts. These lakes form when people build dams. There are also natural rivers and streams that run through parts of the desert.

No two deserts are alike. Desert rock has different kinds of minerals. These rocks can be quite colorful. Desert soils are made up of sand, gravel, and clay.

🎧 When it rains in the desert, dry streams fill with water.

There is some rainfall in the desert. Rain usually occurs only a few months of the year. When it rains it pours. Rain hits ground that is hot and dry from the sun. The water moves fast. In minutes it can flood a dry streambed.

Sometimes it snows high in the mountains. When the snow melts it flows down into the desert valleys.

🎧 Las Vegas, Nevada was once a small desert town. It grew after the Hoover Dam was built nearby.

Hoover Dam in Nevada was built to control and use water from the Colorado River. The dam keeps the river from flooding. Farms get water from the dam. Electric power comes from the dam too.

Today more people are moving to the desert. More people are visiting too. They all need water. That's why it is important to find ways to save it.

Maybe if everyone helps out, there will be enough water for all.

How People Get Water

People also live in the desert. Some like the climate. Some like to be near nature. Some have jobs that draw them there.

People who live near the desert need water to drink. They also need it for electric power.

⊎ Hoover Dam went into full power in 1936.

Did You Know ...

Hoover Dam is named for our thirty-first President, Herbert Hoover. He worked hard to see that the dam was built.

© 2007 Macmillan/McGraw-Hill

Water in the Desert

Water from snow is very important to the plants and animals that live in the desert. Without it, they could not **survive** during the long, hot, dry spells when no rain falls. **Adapting** to this changing weather is how they survive.

ᴑ The La Sal Mountains in the state of Utah are surrounded by desert.

It's a Mirage

If you travel on a desert road on a hot day, you might see what looks like a pool of water up ahead.

When you get to that spot, you find that the water is not there. This trick on the eye is called a mirage. Light rays from the sun bend in the air before they hit the ground. This makes the mirage.

CHAPTER 1

How Desert Plants Get Water

Plants need water. How do desert plants survive with so little of it?

Cactus plants thrive in the desert. These plants have thick skins that have a waxy coat. This helps stop water loss. Their underground roots take in a lot of water at once. Their big stems can hold the water for a long time.

A saguaro cactus can take in a ton ↻ of water in a single day.

Seeds

Plants make seeds, and the desert sands are full of them. Some seeds have tough coats. When the rains come, the water bounces the seeds over hard rocky ground. The seed coats break and they sprout and grow.

Water in the Desert

↻ Snakes sleep during the heat of the day, and at night they grab a meal. They also get their water from their dinner.

Foxes and mountain ↻ lions hunt at night too. They drink from pools of water anywhere they can find them.

↻ This owl makes its home in the ground. It also hunts at night. Its food has enough water in it for the owl to survive.

In the desert sun, water **evaporates** quickly. To keep cool many desert animals hunt for food at night.

© 2007 Macmillan/McGraw-Hill

Other desert plants have very long roots to help them **absorb** water. One such plant is the mesquite (muh-SKEET). Its roots are over 100 feet long.

Some desert plants survive by losing their leaves in the summer. These plants go into a state of rest. They wake up again during the winter rains. One of these is the ocotillo (oh-kuh-TEE-yoh). In summer, it looks dead. But when it rains, its tiny leaves sprout. Pretty orange flowers bloom at the tops of its long stalks. Its branches are covered with sticky sap. This helps to stop water loss.

↻ Here is what a mesquite plant looks like.

The ocotillo plant is ↻ sometimes called candlewood.

CHAPTER 2

How Desert Animals Get Water

Animals need the rain too. Desert frogs and toads lay their eggs in pools of rainwater. The tadpoles quickly grow into adults. Soon the hot sun bakes the earth dry. The water drains away. The adult toads and frogs survive by going underground. They stay there for a year or more. They rest and wait for the rains.

A desert frog has ↻ a rapid growth period followed by a long hibernation period.

A kangaroo rat lives off water in its own body. It also saves water. It builds an underground home or burrow. When the rat breathes, it gives off some water droplets. This water stays inside the burrow.

Pack rats store seeds and nuts in their burrows. The seeds and nuts absorb water from the air. This helps pack rats get enough to drink. They chew on a cactus plant only if they are suffering from thirst. Those cactus spines are sharp.

⋒ A pack rat tries to satisfy its thirst.

Many birds live in the desert. There are owls, hawks, and roadrunners. Desert birds get all their water from the bugs, lizards, and small animals they eat.

The Gambel quail digs ↻ up seeds from the ground. It gets water from seeds.

Word Workout

© Macmillan/McGraw-Hill

(fold here)

WORDS TO KNOW

aisles	annual	expensive	innocent
package	politely	potential	wrapping

Party! Party! Let's use the words to talk about a party. What kind of party will it be? Who will come? When will the party be?

SPELLING WORDS

loop	clue	gloom	goose	blue
mules	cubes	true	shoe	tube
rude	stew	look	shook	spoon

Memory Game Take a quick look at the spelling words. I'm going to give you one of the six spelling patterns: **oo, ue, u-e, oe, ew,** and **oo-e.** Can you remember a spelling word with those letters? Spell the word. When you've run out of words, you can take another quick look. Would you like to test me next?

Home-School Connection

Dear Family Member:

Steven is happy that his aunt is coming to visit. That's how *The Jones Family Express* begins. He wants to get her a present, but he doesn't have much time. He goes to a store to look for a gift, but he doesn't see anything there. I can tell that Steven thinks his aunt is very special because he is looking for just the right present. The author doesn't say that, but the clues are right there. They let me make inferences. I wonder what gift Steven will find? Will it be special?

This Week's Skills

Comprehension: make inferences

Vocabulary: homophones—words that sound the same but are spelled differently

Spelling/Phonics: words with **oo, ue, u-e, oe, ew,** and **oo-e**

Name _____

Greeting Cards

Let's talk about the front of each card. Who would we send this card to? Why? Then we can write a greeting for it.

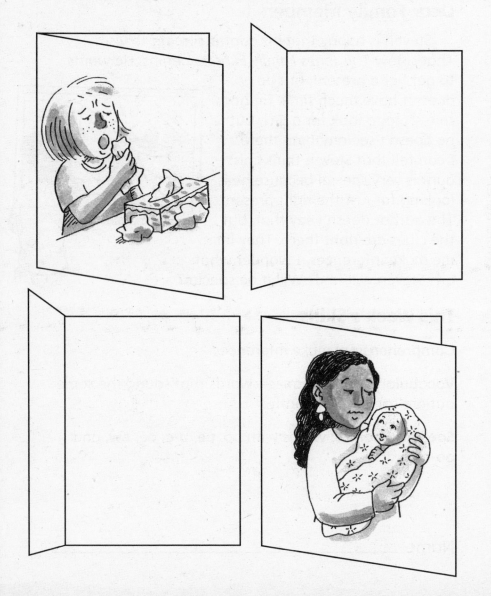

Ejercicio de palabras

PALABRAS DE VOCABULARIO

aisles	annual	expensive	innocent
package	politely	potential	wrapping

¡Fiesta! ¡Fiesta! Usemos las palabras para hablar acerca de una fiesta. ¿Qué tipo de fiesta será? ¿Quién irá? ¿Cuándo será la fiesta?

PALABRAS DE ORTOGRAFÍA

loop	clue	gloom	goose	blue
mules	cubes	true	shoe	tube
rude	stew	look	shook	spoon

Juego de memoria Echa un vistazo a las palabras de ortografía. Te voy a dar uno de los siguientes seis patrones de ortografía: **oo, ue, u-e, oe, ew** y **oo-e**. ¿Puedes recordar una palabra de ortografía con esas letras? Deletrea la palabra. Una vez que termines las palabras, puedes echar otro vistazo de nuevo. ¿Te gustaría tomarme una prueba?

© Macmillan/McGraw-Hill

(fold here)

Conexión con el hogar

Queridos familiares:

Steven está contento que su tía viene de visita. Así es cómo comienza *The Jones Family Express.* Él quiere darle un regalo pero no tiene mucho tiempo. Va a una tienda a buscar un regalo pero no ve nada allí. Puedo ver que Steven piensa que su tía es muy especial porque está buscando un regalo justo para ella. El autor no dice eso, pero las pistas están ahí mismo y me dejan hacer inferencias. Me pregunto qué regalo encontrará Steven. ¿Será algo especial?

Destrezas de la semana

Comprensión: hacer inferencias

Vocabulario: palabras homófonas—palabras que suena similar pero deletrea diferente

Ortografía/Fonética: palabras con **oo, ue, u-e, oe, ew** y **oo-e**

Nombre_____

Tarjetas de saludo

Hablemos acerca de la portada de cada tarjeta. ¿A quién le enviaríamos esta tarjeta? ¿Por qué? Luego, podemos escribir un saludo para alguien en esa tarjeta.

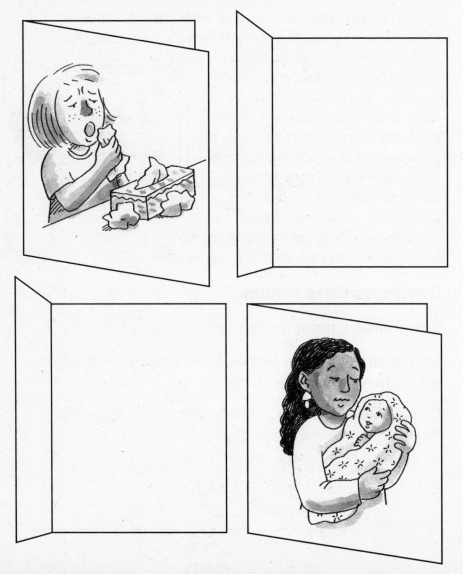

Comprehension Check

Summarize the Story

Use an Inference Chart to record clues about the story. What do Marie's actions tell you about her character? Then summarize the story.

Clues	Inference

Think and Compare

1. Reread page 4. What can you tell about Marie's feelings for Rosie? *(Make Inferences)*

2. What have you learned about preparing for a hurricane from reading this story? *(Apply)*

3. Why is it important for people to be prepared for storms? *(Synthesize)*

Storm Surprise

by S.W. Gonzalez

illustrated by Bob Doucet

Table of Contents

Chapter 1 Gray Skies

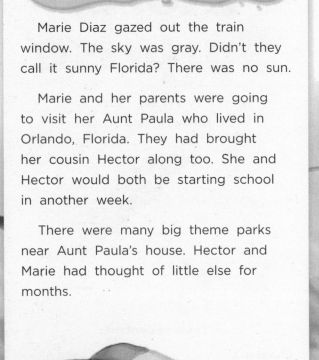

Marie Diaz gazed out the train window. The sky was gray. Didn't they call it sunny Florida? There was no sun.

Marie and her parents were going to visit her Aunt Paula who lived in Orlando, Florida. They had brought her cousin Hector along too. She and Hector would both be starting school in another week.

There were many big theme parks near Aunt Paula's house. Hector and Marie had thought of little else for months.

2

© 2007 Macmillan/McGraw-Hill

They heard a sound. "It sounds like Rosie, but I don't see her," Hector said.

Aunt Paula sloshed through the water and pushed aside the fallen branches. "Look," she said happily.

Rosie was under the porch. She stood on a floating plank of wood and barked.

Aunt Paula crouched and got Rosie. The sun broke through the clouds as she handed the puppy to Marie. "I knew she'd be all right," said Hector.

Marie smiled. Perhaps this hurricane holiday was going to work out just fine.

15

Marie was glad the storm was over but she felt awful about Rosie. "Let's look for her," Hector said.

"I'll come too," Aunt Paula offered. "Breakfast can wait." She shared her extra pairs of boots with them. They were too large but it didn't matter.

"I don't care about the theme parks anymore," Marie said. "I'll be happy if we find Rosie."

14

© 2007 Macmillan/McGraw-Hill

Hector slept in the seat beside Marie. Marie's mother and father had seats behind them.

The aisles in the train were so narrow, her father, on his way back from the dining car, had to stop and let the conductor go by.

"How are you two doing?" the conductor asked Marie.

"Fine, thanks," Marie said politely.

3

Marie then asked her dad, "How's Rosie?" She was talking about her tiny black poodle. Her mom was holding the tiny dog in a baby carrier around her neck.

"She's just fine," Mr. Diaz told her. "Rosie is sleeping."

Her parents wanted to leave Rosie home, but Marie insisted that her new puppy was too young to leave behind. She was so small she'd be no trouble at all. Her parents finally agreed.

4

© 2007 Macmillan/McGraw-Hill

Her father put his hand on her shoulder. Cold rain dropped down his arm. "I'm sorry," he said. "It's not safe for me to be out there looking for her any longer."

Marie nodded. She didn't want anything to happen to her father. But she couldn't stop worrying about Rosie.

That night the family slept on the couches and chairs in the living room. Everyone felt safer being together.

In the morning Marie sat up and listened. She didn't hear any rain or wind.

Aunt Paula came out of the kitchen. "There are cereal bars for breakfast, she said, as she pulled the wrapping off the package. Marie and Hector went to the kitchen.

13

Chapter 3 The Rescue

A while later, Marie's father returned without Rosie. He was soaked and his hair had been blown by the wind. "I can't find her," he said. "I called to her but the wind is loud. She might not have heard me."

Marie gasped. "Oh, no!" she cried. This time she couldn't stop her tears. Rosie was out there in the hurricane!

12

© 2007 Macmillan/McGraw-Hill

Marie spent the last hours of the trip reading. Her new book was so interesting that it made the hours pass quickly.

Soon she felt the train slow down. Her heart began to beat fast. She shook Hector's arm. "Wake up. We're here," she said.

"Huh?" he mumbled, still half asleep. "We're here?" He rubbed his eyes.

Now both children looked out the window. They saw that it was raining. Marie tried not to show her disappointment.

5

Mr. Diaz ran through the rain to rent a car. The rain was coming down harder now, and it was windy. Everyone was getting wet even though they stood under an awning. Rosie barked from under Mrs. Diaz's jacket.

"I'd better walk her," Mrs. Diaz said. She dug into her big purse, pulled out an umbrella, and opened it. Almost at once a strong wind grabbed the open umbrella. It snapped inside out. Then it blew right out of Mrs. Diaz's hand. Marie and Hector watched the umbrella sail off into the wind. The weather was getting worse.

"I'll walk Rosie," Hector offered. He put the hood of his sweatshirt over his head as Mrs. Diaz handed him the dog.

"I'll come with you," Marie said. She and Hector stepped out into the wind and rain. Rosie barked happily.

6

A cardboard box blew past the open door. Rosie barked at it and then dashed out after it. Marie's father ran out into the storm after the dog.

Marie and Hector looked at one another, speechless and scared.

Aunt Paula came into the room and asked, "Where's your dad?"

"He went to get Rosie," Marie said. "She's out there."

11

"I think this is pretty cool," said Hector.

"What an innocent child," said Aunt Paula, smiling. "Hurricanes cause a lot of damage. It's so expensive to fix everything up afterwards. We're lucky because we don't have to go to a shelter this time."

Something banged against a board that covered a living room window. A loud cracking sound made Marie cover her ears. "The tree in back must have blown over," Aunt Paula said.

"I'd better take a look," Marie's father said, as he headed for the door. Marie and Hector, and Rosie followed.

Mr. Diaz pushed opened the door. He leaned out, trying to see the fallen tree on the roof. Rosie barked at a broken branch that blew past.

Marie and Hector watched, amazed at the force of the wind.

© 2007 Macmillan/McGraw-Hill

Chapter 2 The Hurricane

Mr. Diaz pulled the car into Aunt Paula's driveway. Aunt Paula ran out to greet them. Wind blew her hair around her head. Rain soaked her red jacket.

"I'm glad to see you, big brother," she said to Mr. Diaz. "You're just in time to help me board up the windows." She smiled at Marie, Hector, and Mrs. Diaz. "I'm sorry to greet you this way, but Hurricane Rob is coming. The TV weather person says it has the potential to do a lot of damage."

"Don't worry about us," Mrs. Diaz told her. "We're glad to help."

"Thanks," said Aunt Paula. "I have wood, nails, and other things we need in the garage."

Everyone got to work. Mr. Diaz started nailing the boards over the windows. The others carried bottles of water, canned food, and flashlights from the garage.

The wind blew the cap off of Hector's head. He chased it but it landed in a tree. "Wow!" he said. "That's some wild wind!"

The wind howled. Rain pounded the roof. "All theme parks will remain closed until Hurricane Rob passes," the weatherperson said.

© 2007 Macmillan/McGraw-Hill

Storm Surprise

Marie kept herself from crying, but it was just so unfair. She and Hector had looked forward to going to the theme parks for so long.

"I'm sorry kids," Aunt Paula said as she turned off the radio. "Hurricane season is an annual event. Some years it hits us hard, and other years it's not as bad."

Word Workout

© Macmillan/McGraw-Hill

WORDS TO KNOW

illustrate	instance	sketches
style	suggestions	textures

Word Choice Tell me what words you would use to talk about illustrators. Then let's try to use the words in sentences that describe something illustrators do first, second, and third.

SPELLING WORDS

spoiled	point	voice	choice
boiled	coins	noise	loyal
soil	toil	joyful	enjoys
coy	foil	soybean	

Speed Spell I'll say each word from the list for you to spell. I'll give you five seconds to spell each word correctly. If you misspell a word, I'll say "OY!" so you have a chance to spell it again.

---(fold here)---

Home-School Connection

Dear Family Member:

What Do Illustrators Do? takes you step by step through how an artist goes about illustrating. I was surprised to learn that a lot goes on before illustrators actually draw the pictures. They think about what they want to show and how they want to draw it. Sometimes they get models to pose for them. There are many things illustrators do, and this book takes you through the whole process.

This Week's Skills

Comprehension: sequence

Vocabulary: context clues

Spelling/Phonics: words with **oy** and **oi**

Name _____

As Easy As 1, 2, 3

Together, let's make up a short story, one that we can tell in six sentences. We'll write each sentence in one of the boxes, but we'll write them out of order. Then, we can find another family member or a friend to tell us our story in order.

Ejercicio de palabras

PALABRAS DE VOCABULARIO

illustrate	instance	sketches
style	suggestions	textures

Escoger palabras Dime qué palabras usarías para hablar acerca de los ilustradores. Luego, tratemos de usar las palabras en oraciones que describan algo que los ilustradores hacen primero, segundo y tercero.

PALABRAS DE ORTOGRAFÍA

spoiled	point	voice	choice
boiled	coins	noise	loyal
soil	toil	joyful	enjoys
coy	foil	soybean	

¡Rápido! Voy a decir una palabra de ortografía y la deletreas. Tienes cinco segundas para deletrearla correctamente. Si no deletreas correctamente, voy a decir "OY!" y puedes deletrearla otra vez.

© Macmillan/McGraw-Hill

(fold here)

Conexión con el hogar

Queridos familiares:

El libro *What Do Illustrators Do?* muestra paso a paso cómo lo hace un artista. Me sorprendí al saber que muchas cosas ocurren antes de que los ilustradores finalmente hagan sus dibujos. Ellos piensan acerca de lo que quieren mostrar y cómo quieren dibujarlo. A veces tienen modelos que posan para ellos. Hay muchos tipos de cosas que ellos hacen y este libro te lleva por todo el proceso.

Destrezas de la semana

Comprensión: orden de los sucesos

Vocabulario: claves de contexto

Ortografía/Fonética: palabras con **oy** y **oi**

Nombre _____

Tan fácil como decir 1, 2, 3

Vamos a escribir juntos un cuento corto, uno que podamos narrar en seis oraciones. Escribiremos cada oración en cada uno de los recuadros, pero no las escribiremos en orden. Luego, podemos buscar a otro miembro de la familia o un amigo para que nos narre el cuento en orden.

Comprehension Check

Summarize

Use a Sequence Chart to record the basic steps in creating a lifelike drawing. Then use the chart to summarize what you learned about drawing faces.

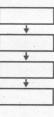

Think and Compare

1. Reread page 8. To add texture to portraits, what does the author suggest you do first? Next? *(Identify Sequence of Events)*

2. Do you have a favorite story that you would like to illustrate? How would your illustrations of people be different from the ones in this book? *(Apply)*

3. What makes cartoons funny? For instance, what makes you think that your favorite cartoon character is funny? *(Evaluate)*

Drawing Faces

by Lisa Norby   illustrated by Jane Whitney

Table of Contents

Introduction

Most of us wish that we could draw people. Whether you want to illustrate a story or design a poster, the ability to draw people comes in handy.

We all look at faces every day. But beginning artists still have trouble putting what they see on paper. For instance, they often draw the eyes too low. They make the top of the head too small. The people they draw look odd.

Try for this   Not this

Glossary

iris *(IGH-ris)* the colored part of the eye. The iris is a circular ring around the pupil. ***(page 6)***

nostril *(NOS-truhl)* an opening that makes it possible to breathe through the nose. Each of us has two nostrils. ***(page 7)***

portrait *(PAWR-trit)* a painting or photograph of a person ***(page 4)***

pupil *(PYEW-puhl)* the dark circular opening at the center of the eye ***(page 6)***

texture *(TEKS-chur)* the look and feel of something ***(page 8)***

Index

Conclusion

Drawing is a lot like reading and writing. It takes practice to do it well.

The more you draw, the more creative you will be. You will begin to develop your own personal style.

You don't need special supplies to learn to draw. All you really need to get started is an ordinary pencil and a good eraser. Use any kind of plain white paper.

It's a good idea to start by copying other drawings and photographs. You will get better with practice. Then you can surprise your friends and family by drawing them.

Did You Know?

Before photography was invented, artists went from door to door, offering to paint people's pictures for money.

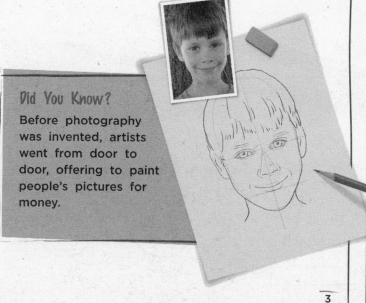

Chapter 1
Getting Started

Some faces are round. Some are square. Some people have small noses and pointed chins. Others have long noses and high foreheads. Even so, faces are more alike than different. To make **portraits** look real, you need to get the shapes right.

Picture a girl named Jenny. To draw Jenny, try following these easy steps.

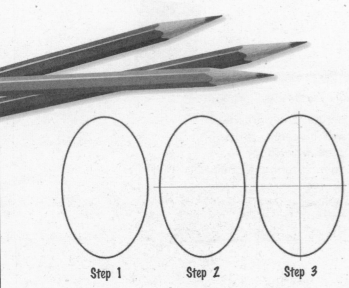

Step 1   Step 2   Step 3

Cartoon figures do not have to be lifelike at all. They may have very round heads or very square ones. Cartoonists even draw faces in the shape of baseballs or footballs!

Cartoon figures don't look real. But they still seem to have human feelings. A good artist will find simple ways to show joy, sadness, and surprise.

Did You Know?
Cartoonist Charles Schulz really did have a friend named Charlie Brown. The real Charlie was the model for the famous Peanuts character.

Chapter 4
Drawing with Style

Drawing isn't just about making a lifelike picture. It is also a way for artists to express themselves. Every artist has a different style.

For instance, a fashion illustrator may use just a few lines to draw a face.

© 2007 Macmillan/McGraw-Hill

Drawing Faces

1 First, draw an oval.

2 Draw a light horizontal line halfway between the top and bottom of the oval.

3 Now draw a vertical line.

4 Next, draw three ovals along the middle of the horizontal line. The middle oval is there to measure the distance between Jenny's eyes. You will erase it later on.

5 Now draw a triangle where the nose will be. The base of the triangle is about as wide as the middle oval.

6 Finally, draw a line halfway between the base of the triangle and the chin. The mouth will be just above this line.

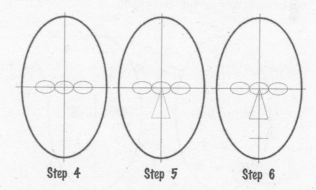

Step 4   Step 5   Step 6

Chapter 2
Drawing Jenny

Now you are ready to draw Jenny. Add the features one by one. Try to draw lightly. Don't be afraid to erase and start over. You can make as many sketches as you want.

First, draw the eyes. Notice that the colored part of the eye has two parts. The center, or **pupil**, is very dark. The outer circle, or **iris**, will be lighter.

Next, add the outer parts of the eye. You will need two lines for the eyelid and one for the lower edge of the eye. Look at the shape of the eyebrows. Everyone's eyebrows are a bit different.

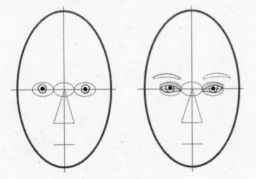
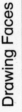

Your drawing of Jenny is almost finished. Erase all the leftover lines that you don't need. Now you are done!

Are you happy with your work? If not, don't give up. Decide which parts of the picture you like least. Did you have trouble with the nose? If so, pay attention to how noses look in photographs. Notice how other artists draw them. Try drawing more of them.

Working artists draw lots of sketches. That is how they try out new ideas.

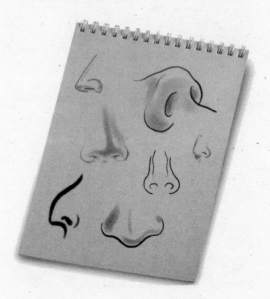

Use a pencil to add more shading.

Soft shading will make Jenny look pretty. Rub the shaded area with your finger to blend and soften the lines.

Thicker, darker lines give the picture a rougher look.

For really deep shadows, draw lines that go in two directions. This is called cross-hatching.

Did You Know?

Ancient Egyptian painters did not draw faces from the front. They painted people in profile, as they would look if seen from the side.

Noses can be hard to draw. Here are some suggestions. Try drawing just the tip of the nose and the **nostrils**. Then round off the lower sides of the triangle. Use shading to show the shape of the nose.

Chapter 3
Adding Details

Once you have a sketch of Jenny's face, you can add shading and **texture**.

Use texture to draw Jenny's hair. She has wavy hair. Draw it using long, flowing lines. You can't draw every hair. Draw just enough to show the shape of her hairdo.

Just for fun, try drawing Jenny with a different hairdo. Give her short, spiky hair and bangs. Use short pencil strokes. Move your pencil in the direction the hair grows.

Don't forget to draw Jenny's ears, too.

© 2007 Macmillan/McGraw-Hill

Drawing Faces

Get ready to add shading. Imagine that there is a lamp to the left of your drawing. The left side of your picture will be lighter. The right side will have more shadows.

Use shading on Jenny's eyelids. Make her upper lip a little darker than her lower lip.

Did You Know?
For hundreds of years, people have wondered if the Mona Lisa is happy or sad. Artist Leonardo da Vinci created the mystery by keeping the corners of her mouth in the shadows.

Word Workout

WORDS TO KNOW

ingredient	magnificent	tasty
masterpiece	recipes	

Compare and Contrast I'll choose a vocabulary word and you can tell me what it means. Then we'll try to use the word in sentences that compare or contrast. For example, "I think spinach is a tasty vegetable. I think lettuce tastes better than spinach."

SPELLING WORDS

taught	caused	bought	drawing	squawk
bawls	yawn	lawn	hawks	paused
salt	coughing	halls	hauls	crawled

Speed Spell I'm going to give you words to spell. At the end of two minutes, we can see how many words you spelled. Do you want to do it again to see if you can spell more words in two minutes?

Dear Family Member:

In class this week, I'm reading *Cook-a-Doodle-Doo*, a story about a rooster who is the great-grandson of the Little Red Hen. Unlike the folk tale about the Little Red Hen, Rooster has animals that want to help him bake a cake. It's fun to keep seeing how the stories are alike and different. Many pages in the story are like a recipe book. They teach how to bake. It's fun to compare the real recipe with what the animals do.

This Week's Skills

Comprehension: compare and contrast

Vocabulary: idioms

Spelling/Phonics: words with the vowel sound in *saw*

Name _____

(fold here)

I'm Like You.
No, You're Not!

Let's see how many differences and similarities we can find for the following.

How are a computer and a pencil alike?

What is different about a strawberry and a blueberry?

How are a house and a trailer alike?

What is the same about a horse and a cat?

What is different about running and walking?

Me and You

Let's talk about the ways in which we are alike and the ways in which we are different. What is your favorite food? Sport? How old are you? Then we'll fill in the charts below.

What's Different?	
Me	You

What's the Same?
Both of Us

188

Ejercicio de palabras

PALABRAS DE VOCABULARIO

ingredient magnificent tasty

masterpiece recipes

Comparar y contrastar Voy a escoger una palabra de vocabulario y tú me dirás lo que significa. Luego, intentaremos usar la palabra en oraciones que comparen y contrasten. Por ejemplo: I think spinach is a tasty vegetable. I think lettuce tastes better than spinach.

PALABRAS DE ORTOGRAFÍA

taught caused bought drawing squawk

bawls yawn   lawn hawks paused

salt   coughing halls hauls crawled

Ortografía veloz Te voy a dar unas palabras para deletrear. Después de dos minutos, vamos a ver cuántas palabras deletreaste. ¿Quieres hacerlo de nuevo para ver si puedes deletrear más palabras en dos minutos?

(fold here)

Conexión con el hogar

Queridos familiares:

En la clase estoy leyendo esta semana *Cook-a-Doodle-Doo*, un cuento acerca de un gallo que es el bisnieto de la gallinita roja. Rooster tiene amigos que lo quieren ayudar a hornear un pastel, no como en el cuento de La gallinita roja. Es divertido ver cómo los cuentos son parecidos y diferentes. Muchas páginas del cuento son parecidas a un libro de recetas. Te enseñan cómo hornear. Es divertido comparar la receta real con las cosas que hacen los animales.

Destrezas de la semana

Comprensión: comparar y contrastar

Vocabulario: expresiones idiomáticas

Ortografía/Fonética: palabras con el sonido vocal en *saw*

Nombre _____

Soy como tú.
¡No, no lo eres!

Hablemos de las diferencias y las semejanzas entre los siguientes objetos

How are a computer and a pencil alike?

What is different about a strawberry and a blueberry?

How are a house and a trailer alike?

What is the same about a horse and a cat?

What is different about running and walking?

Tú y yo

Hablemos acerca de las cosas en las que somos parecidos y en las que somos diferentes. ¿Cuál es tu comida favorita? ¿Tu deporte favorito? ¿Cuántos años tienes? Escribe tus ideas en la tabla de abajo.

What's Different?	
Me	You

What's the Same?
Both of Us

Comprehension Check

Summarize

Use a Venn Diagram to compare and contrast the foods that you just read about. Then use the diagram to summarize the information in this book.

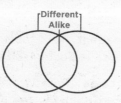

Think and Compare

1. Reread pages 6–9. How were the discovery of ice pops and of chocolate chip cookies the same? How were they different? *(Compare and Contrast)*

2. Which of the foods mentioned in this book is your favorite? Why? *(Evaluate)*

3. Food is important to all people around the world. Yet many people go hungry every day. What do you think might be a good way to help them? *(Evaluate)*

Oops!

Food Surprises

by Doris Licameli

Table of Contents

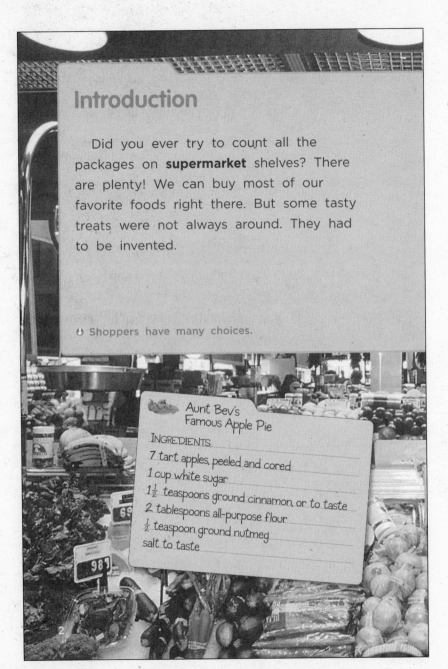

Introduction

Did you ever try to count all the packages on **supermarket** shelves? There are plenty! We can buy most of our favorite foods right there. But some tasty treats were not always around. They had to be invented.

⏻ Shoppers have many choices.

Aunt Bev's
Famous Apple Pie

INGREDIENTS:

7 tart apples, peeled and cored

1 cup white sugar

$1\frac{1}{2}$ teaspoons ground cinnamon, or to taste

2 tablespoons all-purpose flour

$\frac{1}{2}$ teaspoon ground nutmeg

salt to taste

Oops! Food Surprises

Glossary

grain *(GRAYN)* the seed of wheat, corn, rice, oats, and other cereal plants *(page 4)*

patient *(PAY-shuhnt)* a person under the care of a doctor *(page 4)*

recipe *(RES-uh-pee)* a list of ingredients and instructions for making something to eat or drink *(page 3)*

rennet *(REN-nit)* an extract from the stomach of an animal used to curdle milk *(page 13)*

supermarket *(SEW-puhr-mahr-kit)* a large store that sells foods and household goods *(page 2)*

Index

Conclusion

Who knows what new foods will come next? Magnificent surprises can happen to anyone. Maybe you will invent something wonderful. Just don't forget to write down the ingredients. You don't want to forget the recipe!

Everyone enjoys a good meal. What's your favorite?

Most foods are made by using **recipes**. Each ingredient is listed along with an exact measurement to use.

But some great treats were magnificent surprises. Grand things happened when people tried to do one thing but something else came about instead. Most times, the inventors were not even scientists. They were ordinary people, even kids.

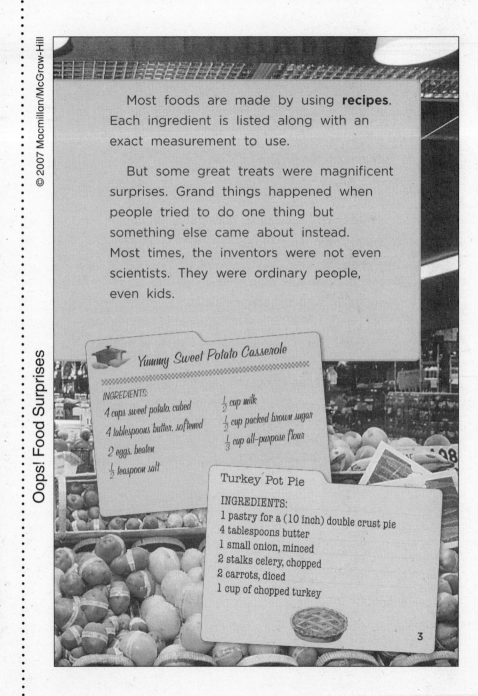

Yummy Sweet Potato Casserole

INGREDIENTS:

4 cups sweet potato, cubed

4 tablespoons butter, softened

2 eggs, beaten

$\frac{1}{2}$ teaspoon salt

$\frac{1}{2}$ cup milk

$\frac{1}{2}$ cup packed brown sugar

$\frac{1}{3}$ cup all-purpose flour

Turkey Pot Pie

INGREDIENTS:

1 pastry for a (10 inch) double crust pie

4 tablespoons butter

1 small onion, minced

2 stalks celery, chopped

2 carrots, diced

1 cup of chopped turkey

Chapter 1
Corn Flakes

In the 1890s Will Keith Kellogg worked at a clinic with his brother John. It was a special hospital in Battle Creek, Michigan. No meat was served to the **patients** staying there. The Kellogg brothers didn't think eating meat was healthy. They believed people should eat only fruit, vegetables, and **grains**.

Battle Creek, ↻ Michigan is where the Kellogg brothers lived.

Vegetables

Grains

Fruits

4

A long time ago, a man set out on a journey across the desert. He'd brought along milk in a pouch made from a sheep's stomach. The blazing sun made the man thirsty. But when he opened the pouch, the man was surprised. The hot milk had mixed with something in the lining of the sheep's stomach called **rennet** (REN-nit). It turned the milk into lumps of cheese!

Big Cheese

Sometimes a person is called a "big wheel" or a "big cheese." When these terms were first used, they described people who were rich enough to buy a whole wheel of cheese.

◠ Over 2,000 types of cheese are made around the world.

Chapter 5
Cheese

What would we do without cheese? We wouldn't have macaroni and cheese or pizza. It's a good thing a mistake happened a long time ago in the desert. An old legend tells us how cheese may have come about.

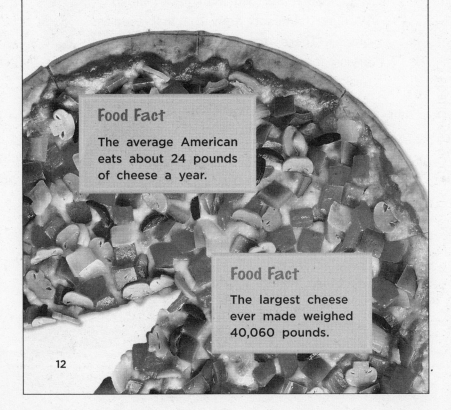

Food Fact

The average American eats about 24 pounds of cheese a year.

Food Fact

The largest cheese ever made weighed 40,060 pounds.

12

Will Kellogg owned a ranch which he called Kellogg Ranch. This photograph shows him holding a birthday party for his twin colts.

One day, Will was boiling a pot of wheat but he got called away. The wheat grew cold and hard. Will forced it through a rolling machine anyway. Out came broken flakes. But the crunchy flakes turned out to be tasty. Will hurried to do the same thing using corn. Corn flakes were a success! They became a popular breakfast cereal. Will Kellogg became a wealthy man.

Food Fact

A single bushel of corn contains about 73,000 kernels.

5

Chapter 2
Ice Pops

Even kids can be inventors. Frank Epperson was eleven years old when he proved it! One night he mixed powdered fruit flavor in a cup of soda water. He stirred it with a stick. That's how people made fruit drinks in 1905. But after a sip or two, Frank left his drink on the back porch.

The night grew very cold. By morning, Frank had a magnificent surprise. His fruit soda had frozen to the stick.

Food Fact

Frank Epperson applied for a patent on this invention in 1923.

© 2007 Macmillan/McGraw-Hill

Raisins arrived in the United States in the 1800s. The San Joaquin Valley in California had the perfect conditions for growing and drying grapes. The growing season was long. There was plenty of sunshine.

In 1876 a Scottish immigrant named William Thompson grew the first seedless grapes. These grapes were great for drying into raisins. They become perfect raisins, the raisins we know today.

Raisins are healthful ↻ snack foods.

Food Fact

Today, 95% of California's raisins are made from Thompson's seedless grapes.

Chapter 4
Raisins

Many people believed that raisins were a lucky accident. Humans first came upon raisins in Ancient Times. They found some grapes drying on a vine under the hot sun. And they were delicious.

Several hundred years later people started to grow grapes just to turn them into raisins. The land around Persia (now Iraq and Iran) had the perfect climate for this. By 900 B.C. growers were trading with Greece and Rome. By the 1300s raisins were an important food in Europe.

Food Fact

Greeks and Romans decorated places of worship with raisins. They also handed them out to the winners in sporting events. Romans also used raisins to cure illness.

Area of Detail

Greece
Black Sea
Mediterranean Sea
PERSIAN EMPIRE
Ecbatana
Persepolis
PARSIS
Egypt
Arabia
Indian Ocean

© 2007 Macmillan/McGraw-Hill

Oops! Food Surprises

Food Fact

About three million ice pops are sold each year.

↪ There are more than 30 flavors of ice pops sold today but orange is still the most popular!

Frank showed it to his friends. At first everyone thought Frank had lost his marbles. They thought he was crazy. But after one lick, everyone cheered. Frank's invention was a masterpiece. A work of art! Frank called it an Epsicle. Frank decided to sell the icy treats.

Food Fact

Twin ice pops were created during the Great Depression when many people were very poor. Two kids could share one ice pop.

Chapter 3
Chocolate Chip Cookies

Ruth Wakefield owned the Toll House Inn in 1930. Running the small hotel kept her busy. But she always used her best recipes to make all the meals. The guests especially liked Ruth's tasty desserts. But her most famous dessert happened by mistake.

↻ The Toll House Inn was located on an early toll road between Boston and New Bedford, Massachusetts.

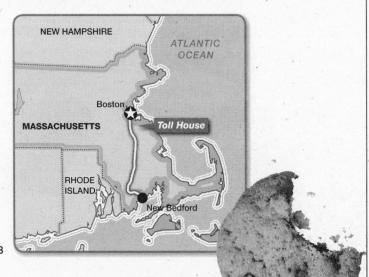

Oops! Food Surprises

While mixing a batch of chocolate cookies one day, Ruth's heart sank. There was no baking chocolate. Instead, she broke a semisweet chocolate bar into small pieces. She mixed them into the dough. But when the cookies came out of the oven, Ruth was surprised. The chocolate bits hadn't melted into the dough. Instead, she'd just made the world's first chocolate chip cookies. Most people thought these cookies were out of this world.

Food Fact

Chocolate chip cookies are the most popular cookies in the United States today.

Word Workout

WORDS TO KNOW

argued	beamed	fabric
possessions	purchased	quarreling

To Market We Go Let's use the words to make up a story about going to a market.

SPELLING WORDS

bow	crowd	plow	louder	town
bounce	found	clouds	proud	couch
ground	shout	round	scout	owl

Ow and Ouch! Let's sort the words into those with **ow** and those with **ou**. Now we can spell the words in each group.

© Macmillan/McGraw-Hill

···(fold here)···

Home-School Connection

Dear Family Member:

In *Seven Spools of Thread*, a father who loves his seven sons is disappointed. The brothers argue all the time. When the father dies, they find out they will not inherit their father's money unless they turn seven spools of thread into gold. I can use two clues. The father loved them, and he wanted them to stop arguing. These clues help me draw a conclusion. The father's strange instruction will bring peace to his children.

This Week's Skills

Comprehension: draw conclusions

Vocabulary: multiple-meaning words

Spelling/Phonics: words with **ow** and **ou**

Name _____

I Conclude That . . .

Let's watch a TV show together. We can look for clues about characters and events, and then make conclusions as we go along. The charts below will help us.

CLUES

A Character

What is the character like?

What does the character say?

What does the character do?

How does the character treat other characters?

Conclusion

I think the character is (for example: wise, silly, kind):

Events

What is the first thing that happens?

Who makes it happen?

What happens next?

Does someone make that happen?

Does the event before this one make it happen?

Conclusions

I think the next thing to happen is (for example: Julio will sell his guitar to get money for his mother's medicine):

Ejercicio de palabras

PALABRAS DE VOCABULARIO

argued	beamed	fabric
possessions	purchased	quarreling

Vamos al mercado Usemos las palabras para inventar un cuento acerca de ir a un mercado.

PALABRAS DE ORTOGRAFÍA

bow	crowd	plow	louder	town
bounce	found	clouds	proud	couch
ground	shout	round	scout	owl

¡Ow y ouch! Clasifiquemos las palabras entre las que tienen las letras **ow** y las que tienen las letras **ou**. Ahora podemos deletrear las palabras de cada grupo.

(fold here)

Conexión con el hogar

Queridos familiares:

En *Seven Spools of Thread*, un padre que ama a sus siete hijos se siente decepcionado. Los hermanos discuten todo el tiempo. Cuando el padre muere, ellos descubren que no iban a heredar el dinero de su padre a menos que conviertan siete carretes de hilo en oro. Puedo usar dos pistas. El padre amaba a sus hijos y quería que ellos dejaran de discutir. Estas pistas me ayudan a sacar una conclusión. El extraño pedido del padre va a traer paz a sus hijos.

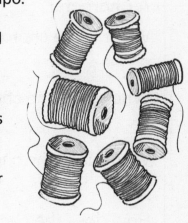

Destrezas de la semana

Comprensión: sacar conclusiones

Vocabulario: palabras con más de un significado

Ortografía/Fonética: palabras con **ow** y **ou**

Nombre_____

En el mundo real

Veamos juntos un programa de televisión. Podemos buscar pistas acerca de los personajes y los sucesos, y luego sacar conclusiones mientras vemos el programa. Las tablas de abajo nos ayudarán.

CLUES

A Character

What is the character like?

What does the character say?

What does the character do?

How does the character treat other characters?

Conclusion

I think the character is (for example: wise, silly, kind):

Events

What is the first thing that happens?

Who makes it happen?

What happens next?

Does someone make that happen?

Does the event before this one make it happen?

Conclusions

I think the next thing to happen is (for example: Julio will sell his guitar to get money for his mother's medicine):

Comprehension Check

Summarize the Story

Use your Conclusion Map to record clues and draw a conclusion about the story. Then use the map to summarize the story. Why does the old man give the diamond to his youngest son?

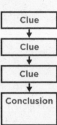

Clue

↓

Clue

↓

Clue

↓

Conclusion

Think and Compare

1. Look back at page 6. What does the oldest son think people need the most? Does this change your opinion of him? Why or why not? *(Draw Conclusions)*

2. Think of a time you did something good for someone. What did you do? *(Apply)*

3. What are some other ways that people can help others? *(Evaluate)*

A True Hero

told by Steven Otfinoski
illustrated by Susan Todd

Table of Contents

Chapter 1
A Father's Challenge

Long ago in Mexico there lived a very old man who had three sons. He wanted to leave them his most prized possessions before he died. So he divided everything equally among the three of them. However, there was one thing he could not divide. This was a valuable diamond he had purchased as a very young man.

2

The old man stood up and embraced his son.

"My son, what you have done is very special. Your brothers have done fine things. Yet we all try to help the poor. And if any of us saw a stranger in trouble, we would try to help. But to help an enemy in danger is something that many people would not do. And to make a friend out of an enemy is something even rarer in this world. My son, you have done this, and you are the truest hero of all!"

And with that the old man handed his surprised son the precious diamond.

15

"He stared up at me at once. He wanted to know what I was doing. I think he was scared that I was going to hurt him. I told him that he should move away from the hill so he wouldn't fall. That made him even more surprised."

The youngest son told them how Pancho had returned from another village and got lost in the dark. He lay down to sleep for the night, but did not know he was at the edge of a hilltop. Then he asked the youngest son why he stopped him from falling.

"I did it because I don't think anyone deserves to be hurt, not even you," the youngest son had said.

"What happened then?" asked his father.

"Pancho and I shook hands and promised to be friends forever," said the youngest son. "Well, that is the good I have done."

14

© 2007 Macmillan/McGraw-Hill

The old man could give the diamond to only one son. Which one should it be? He loved them all equally. Finally he came up with a solution.

The next morning, the old man called his three sons before him.

"My sons, I have a problem," he told them. "I love all three of you, but I can give my most precious possession to only one of you. Therefore, I will give my diamond to the son that best meets my challenge."

3

"The one of you who proves to be a true hero will get the diamond," said the old man.

"That is fair," said the three sons in unison.

"To decide who is the true hero, I will give you a task," said their father. "You are each to go out and do the most good you can in a week's time. Then you are each to return and report what you have done. I will judge who has done the greatest good, and he will get the diamond."

4

© 2007 Macmillan/McGraw-Hill

"Who was he?" asked his father.

"It was no other than Pancho," answered the youngest son.

"Pancho?" asked the oldest son. "The same Pancho who is so mean to you at school?"

"The same Pancho," said the youngest son. "I've argued with him more times than I'd like to remember."

"I hope you gave him what he deserved!" cried the middle son.

"Did you roll him down the hill?" asked the oldest son. "It would serve him right for all he's done to you!"

"I won't lie and say I didn't think about doing it," admitted the youngest son. "Yet I felt sorry for him at the same time. So I gently touched his shoulder and he woke up."

13

"I was walking along the top of a hill when I saw something very strange," began the youngest son. "A person was lying on the hilltop fast asleep in a blanket. If he had moved only a few inches he would have rolled down the hill and certainly hurt himself on the rocks that lay there."

"Go on," said his father. "What happened then?"

"I moved quietly toward the sleeper to gently wake him up and stop him from falling. But as I moved closer, I recognized who he was."

A True Hero

"Very well, father," said the oldest son.

"It is a fair test," said the middle son.

"I will try to do what you say, father," said the youngest son.

"Good," replied their father. "And there must be no quarreling or bad feelings among you when I have made my decision. Now off you go to do good. You only have a week, so use your time wisely."

Chapter 2
The Generous Son

The week passed quickly, and the old man waited eagerly for his sons' return. When they finally arrived, he could hardly wait to hear their reports.

He started with the oldest. "So tell me, son, what have you done this week that was good?" he asked.

The oldest son beamed with the brightest smile.

"Father," he said, "I have made you very proud. I must confess at first I was stumped. I thought and thought and thought about how I could do the most good. I wondered what people needed the most. And then it came to me—money!"

"This is good," said the old man. "Please continue."

© 2007 Macmillan/McGraw-Hill

Chapter 4
The True Hero

The old man motioned to his youngest son.

"Come, it is your turn to tell us what good you have done this week," he said.

The younger son was too embarrassed at first to say anything.

He pulled at the fabric of his shirt as he spoke.

"Come," the old man said impatiently. "Speak up my son."

"What I have done, father," he said at last, "will not mean much to anyone else I suppose, but it means a lot to me."

"Then let us hear it," said the old man. He was quite curious about what his youngest son would say.

"I splashed around in the water until I reached the girl and then pulled her to shore. I put her down on the bank and she came to. I saved her life."

The old man rose from his chair. "This is wonderful!" he exclaimed. "My son, you are a true hero!"

10

"So I divided up all my money and property in half and I gave one half to the poor," said the oldest son.

"This is wonderful!" cried the old man. "You have done very well, my son. I am pleased with your generosity. Now let me see what your brothers have done."

7

Chapter 3
The Brave Son

The old man turned to his middle son.

"Well, son, tell us what you have done that was good," he said.

"I have done something even greater than what my older brother has done," boasted the middle son. "Giving away your money is very good, but to save a life is an even greater good!"

"Save a life!" cried their father. "Please, tell us more, my son."

"I was walking along the riverbank," explained the middle son, "when I heard someone cry. I looked down into the water and saw a little girl in the river, crying for help! I remembered that I could not swim. But when I looked around, there was no one else to save the poor girl. So I leaped into the chilly water."

"This is marvelous!" cried the old man. "Go on, my son."

Word Workout

WORDS TO KNOW

clumps	native	research
shouldn't	sprout	

Word Chain Can we link one word to another? Can we link **clumps** and **research**? What about **shouldn't** and **native**? Let's try all different kinds of links and use both words in a sentence.

SPELLING WORDS

cell	price	cents	city	nice
space	changes	gyms	gentle	gems
giant	pages	age	message	place

Sort and Spell Let's sort the words into those with the **s** sound spelled **c** and those with the **j** sound spelled **g**. Then we can spell the words in each group.

(fold here)

Home-School Connection

Dear Family Member:

"Washington Weed Whackers" is about a harmful plant and a group of kids at an elementary school. The plant is killing other plants and animals on the northwest coast of Washington. The plant is good for other plants and animals in the Northeast. The article tells me how the effects of the plants are different in the two environments. The students in a school on the northwest coast begin an awareness campaign. I wonder if there is something the students in my school could do to help make a needed change.

This Week's Skills

Comprehension: compare and contrast

Vocabulary: contractions

Spelling/Phonics: words with **c** and **g**

Name _____

Be a Detective

We're going to look at each picture and see what's the same in both pictures and what is different. For example, are the kids wearing the same clothes or different clothes? What expressions do they have on their faces? Are they playing the same games? How many comparisons and contrasts can we make?

Ejercicio de palabras

PALABRAS DE VOCABULARIO

clumps   native   research

shouldn't   sprout

Cadena de palabras ¿Podemos conectar una palabra con otra? ¿Podemos conectar **clumps** y **research**? ¿Y conectar **shouldn't** y **native**? Vamos a intentar diferentes tipos de conexiones y usar ambas palabras en una oración.

PALABRAS DE ORTOGRAFÍA

cell	price	cents	city	nice
space	changes	gyms	gentle	gems
giant	pages	age	message	place

Clasifica Clasificamos las palabras que tienen un sonido **s** pero son escrito con una **c** y las que tienen un sonido **j** pero son escrito con una **g**. Luego podemos deletrear las palabras en cada grupo.

© Macmillan/McGraw-Hill

(fold here)

Conexión con el hogar

Queridos familiares:

Washington Weed Whackers es un artículo acerca de una planta dañina y un grupo de niños de una escuela primaria. La planta está matando otras plantas y animales en la costa del noroeste de Washington. Sin embargo, la planta es benigna para otras plantas y animales en el Noreste. El artículo me cuenta cómo los efectos de las plantas son diferentes en los dos medio ambientes. Los estudiantes de una escuela de la costa del noroeste comenzaron con una campaña. Me pregunto si los estudiantes de mi escuela pueden ayudar a cambiar algo que sea necesario cambiar.

Destrezas de la semana

Comprensión: comparar y contrastar

Vocabulario: contracciones

Ortografía/Fonética: palabras con **c** y **g**

Nombre _____

Sé un detective

Vamos a observar cada ilustración y ver qué es igual en ambas ilustraciones y qué es diferente. Por ejemplo: ¿Los niños visten la misma ropa o ropa diferente? ¿Qué expresiones tienen en sus caras? ¿Hay el mismo tipo de árboles en la ilustración o son diferentes?

Comprehension Check

Summarize

Use the photographs to tell about the outdoor activities described in this book. Then list how these activities use natural resources. Use the information to summarize what you learned.

Think and Compare

1. Reread page 10. Compare and contrast what the hikers and loggers think about the forests. *(Compare and Contrast)*

2. Which of our natural resources do you use the most? Explain. *(Apply)*

3. Why is it important for people to learn about our natural resources? What actions can people take to protect our natural resources? *(Evaluate)*

Enjoying Our Natural Resources

by Michael Schuman

Table of Contents

Introduction

It's thrilling to ski down a slope with the wind hitting your cheeks. It's fun to hike in the woods and hear the birds chirping. It's great to feel cool water splashing against your skin on a hot day.

When you go skiing, hiking, or swimming, you are making use of our natural resources.

Enjoying Our Natural Resources

Glossary

harness (*HAHR-nis*) the straps, bands, and other gear used to hold an animal or person *(page 8)*

logger (*LOG-uhr*) a person who cuts down trees *(page 10)*

pollution (*puh-LEW-shuhn*) gases, chemicals, and wastes that make our air, water, or soil dirty *(page 12)*

stalactite (*stuh-LAK-tight*) a piece of stone that looks like an icicle and hangs from the roof of a cave *(page 8)*

stalagmite (*stuh-LAG-might*) a piece of stone shaped like a cone, built up from the floor of a cave *(page 8)*

waste (*WAYST*) material that has been thrown away or is left over *(page 3)*

Index

Conclusion

There are many ways we can enjoy our natural resources and care for them at the same time. People can work together to have laws passed that will help reduce pollution and the cutting down of forests.

If everyone takes part in caring for our resources, people can continue to enjoy these natural wonders.

↻ Some people do their part by picking up litter along highways.

14

The United States has many natural resources for all to enjoy. However, our beautiful land with all its plants and animals needs our care and respect. Some native wildlife is in danger because people have cut down trees for lumber. Some of our waters are dirty with **waste** from factories. The challenge is to find ways to protect our natural resources and enjoy them too.

↻ These hikers enjoy the sights as they hike up a hill.

3

Water and Snow

On hot summer days, people go to ocean beaches or to lakes or rivers. They like to relax, swim, and build sandcastles.

People also like to fish in lakes and streams for bass and trout. And deep-sea fishers sail boats to catch tuna, cod, or other fish in our seas.

↻ Many buildings surround popular beachfronts.

Did You Know . . .

Scientists have found that pollution exists everywhere on Earth, from the largest city to the remote South Pole.

‍ The view from a hang glider can be amazing.

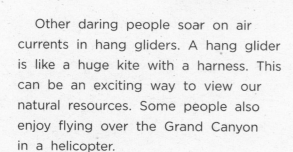

Polluted air has ↪ darkened some views in the Great Smoky Mountains National Park.

Other daring people soar on air currents in hang gliders. A hang glider is like a huge kite with a harness. This can be an exciting way to view our natural resources. Some people also enjoy flying over the Grand Canyon in a helicopter.

But is our air in danger from **pollution**? Factories turn fuel into energy to make goods we need. However, research tells us that some factories release pollutants into the air, water, and soil.

The Grand Canyon is located in Arizona. ↪

12

© 2007 Macmillan/McGraw-Hill

↻ This is a trout.

But people shouldn't leave garbage behind when they visit these places because the trash can get into the water. Fish can become sick. People who eat sick fish can become ill.

Also, sometimes dolphins get caught in fishing nets. People are working to find better ways to catch fish.

↻ Ice-skating and ice fishing are two other ways to enjoy our natural resources.

5

In the winter, making a snowman and building a fort are fun activities. It's also fun to ride sleds or ski down steep hills.

Thrill seekers like to go snowboarding. They race down hills on boards that look like small surfboards. Those who are skilled do tricks with names like "Alley Oop" and "Chicken Salad Air."

Those who like less active sports ride snowmobiles. These vehicles have motors. They move on runners like a sled.

Some people don't like snowmobiles. They believe that these machines release chemicals that pollute the air. Others think they make too much noise.

◔ This family uses a large tube to glide down a snowy hill.

CHAPTER 3 Up in the Air

The air is another natural resource people use for fun. A sailplane has no motor. Flying one of these planes is called soaring. A sailplane floats on air currents, or movements of air. It can travel over 100 miles per hour.

The Soaring Capital of the United States is Elmira, New York. You can fly in any direction there, no matter where the wind blows.

Fast Fact

Elmira is home to the annual U.S. National Soaring Championships and the Soaring Hall of Fame.

Mark Your Trail

It's always a good idea to hike with a buddy or a grownup. Along the trail, stop and make a small pile of stones. Then walk on. Look back, and if you can't see your stone pile, it's time to make another one. Do the same throughout your hike. On your return trip, you can follow the stone piles back to your starting point.

Other people enjoy nature by hiking in mountains, deserts, or the deep, quiet woods.

Hikers and **loggers** do not always agree about how to care for our woods. Some hikers believe that trees should not be cut down, because they are home to wildlife. Loggers say that we need to cut trees down for lumber. Sometimes loggers agree to keep parts of forests from ever being cut.

⬇ Snowboarders love to show off their skills.

In 2001 snowmobiles were banned in two of our big national parks, Yellowstone and Grand Teton. Then in October 2004 the law was changed. Some felt the law was not fair to people who sell and use snowmobiles.

CHAPTER 2 Caves, Rocks, and Woods

Our Earth has beautiful caves that people can explore. Sometimes these explorers wear **harnesses** and hard hats and climb walls inside the caves.

Cave explorers may see unusual rock shapes. A **stalactite** is a form of rock that hangs from the roof or sides of the cave. A **stalagmite** forms on the bottom of the cave.

Did You Know . . .

People who explore or study caves are called speleologists.

This is Devil's Tower ↄ in Wyoming. It's a favorite among rock climbers.

These big clumps of rock sprout and build up slowly over years. They are made of limestone and water.

Other people like to climb rocks. Beginners use ropes and put their hands and feet in holes drilled for their use. Experts make their own routes up the rocks. They've learned to climb without looking down. This, they say, helps to keep them safe.

8

9

Word Workout

WORDS TO KNOW

community   deserve   grownups   interviewed

slogan   thrilled   tour   volunteers

TV Time Let's talk about the meaning of each word. Then we can write a news report for television.

SPELLING WORDS

your   you're   they're   there   sail

sale   beet   beat   its   it's

peace   piece   road   rowed   rode

Here, It's Not What You Hear I'm going to ask you to spell a word in a sentence I give you. Remember, some words sound the same but are spelled differently and mean different things.

(fold here)

Home-School Connection

Dear Family Member:

Angel Arellano is my age and has been in the newspapers and on TV. *Here's My Dollar* tells how Angel learned that the zoo in Fresno was running out of money. Angel wrote to newspapers, talked at different schools, and appeared on talk shows. She asked everyone to donate a dollar to save the zoo and the animals in it. I think the author wants to tell about Angel, but he also wants to show how one person can make a difference.

This Week's Skills

Comprehension: author's purpose

Vocabulary: context clues

Spelling/Phonics: words that sound alike but are spelled differently

Name _____

Why Write?

We can look across and down the columns to find seven words telling us why an author writes a story. We can circle them in the puzzle as we find them.

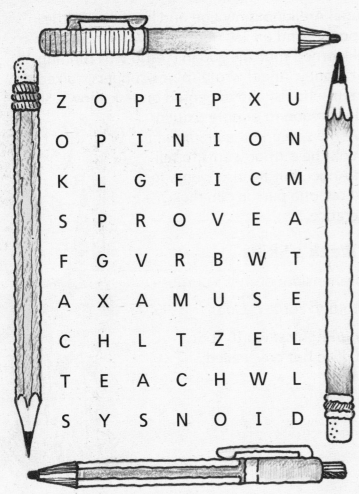

Z	O	P	I	P	X	U
O	P	I	N	I	O	N
K	L	G	F	I	C	M
S	P	R	O	V	E	A
F	G	V	R	B	W	T
A	X	A	M	U	S	E
C	H	L	T	Z	E	L
T	E	A	C	H	W	L
S	Y	S	N	O	I	D

Answers: facts, inform, tell, opinion, prove, amuse, teach

I Want to Write, Because!

Let's look at each picture. What would we write to go with the picture and why would we write it?

224

Ejercicio de palabras

PALABRAS DE VOCABULARIO

community   deserve   grownups   interviewed

slogan   thrilled   tour   volunteers

Tiempo de televisión Hablemos acerca del significado de cada palabra. Luego, podemos escribir un reporte periodístico para televisión.

PALABRAS DE ORTOGRAFÍA

your	you're	they're	there	sail
sale	beet	beat	its	it's
peace	piece	road	rowed	rode

No es lo que escuchas Te voy a pedir que deletrees una palabra en una oración que te voy a dar. Recuerda que algunas palabras suenan igual pero se escriben diferente y significan cosas diferentes.

© Macmillan/McGraw-Hill

(fold here)

Conexión con el hogar

Queridos familiares:

Angel Arellano tiene mi edad y ya apareció en los periódicos y en la televisión. *Here's My Dollar* cuenta cómo Angel se enteró de que el zoológico de Fresno se estaba quedando sin dinero. Angel escribió a los periódicos, dio charlas en diferentes escuelas y apareció en programas de televisión. Pidió a cada persona que done un dólar para salvar el zoológico y a los animales que viven allí. Pienso que el autor quiere hablar sobre Angel, pero también quiere saber cómo una persona puede ayudar a cambiar las cosas.

Destrezas de la semana

Compresión: propósito del autor

Vocabulario: claves de contexto

Ortografía/Fonética: palabras que suenon igual y se escriben diferente

Nombre_____

¿Por qué escribir?

Podemos observar las columnas de manera horizontal y vertical para buscar siete palabras que nos dicen por qué un autor escribe un cuento. Podemos encerrar las palabras en un círculo a medida que las encontramos.

```
Z O P I P X U
O P I N I O N
K L G F I C M
S P R O V E A
T G V R B W T
F X A M U S E
A H L T Z E L
C Y S N O W L
T E A C H I D
S F Z H A J O
```

¡Quiero escribir porque sí!

Observemos cada ilustración. ¿Qué escribiríamos sobre la ilustración y por qué lo escribiríamos?

Comprehension Check

Summarize

Complete an Author's Purpose Chart. Then use the chart to help you summarize Devan's actions.

Think and Compare

1. Why do you think the author wrote about Devan? Explain. *(Evaluate Author's Purpose)*

2. What do you do before you make an oral report to your class? How do you keep yourself calm? *(Apply)*

3. List some things in your neighborhood that could be improved. Explain what has to be done. *(Evaluate)*

PATCHING A PLAYGROUND

by Gail Williams

Table of Contents

Introduction

All playgrounds should be safe. But some of them are not. Sometimes playground **equipment** breaks down. And a broken piece of equipment can be dangerous. Sometimes there are holes in the ground where children can trip and fall. Kids and even grownups don't always recognize these dangers.

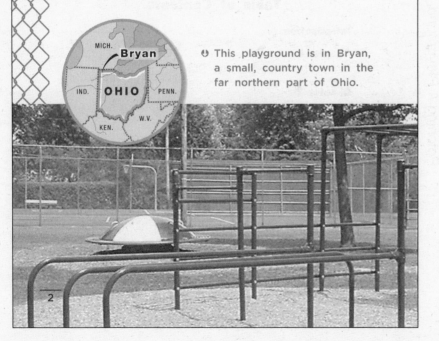

↻ This playground is in Bryan, a small, country town in the far northern part of Ohio.

Glossary

budget *(BUJ-it)* a plan detailing how money will be spent *(page 12)*

catalog *(KAT-uh-log)* a list of goods for sale *(page 12)*

committee *(kuh-MI-tee)* a group of people whose job is to consider, investigate, or take action on a plan *(page 9)*

design *(di-ZIGHN)* created or fashioned for a specific purpose *(page 11)*

equipment *(i-KWIP-muhnt)* tools needed for a specific activity *(page 2)*

symbol *(SIM-buhl)* something chosen to stand for something else *(page 7)*

Index

Conclusion

Devan's concern and hard work have brought her more than a safe playground. The mayor of Bryan, Ohio, named February 16, 2004, as Devan Hickey Day.

↻ On her special day, Devan sat with the mayor.

Devan Hickey's ↻ photograph was in the newspaper.

One nine-year-old girl did spot dangers on a playground, and she decided to take action. She came up with a wonderful plan for making the playground safe. She's Devan Hickey, a fun-loving girl who lives in Bryan, Ohio.

First Devan got all her facts together. Then she reported her plan to a group of people in her community who could help her. She also asked family and friends to help out. She didn't give up until the playground was safe. Read her story.

This is Devan Hickey. ↻

CHAPTER 1

Was the Playground Safe?

One day after a softball game, Devan joined her parents and two-year-old sister on the local playground. That's when Devan took a good look at the playground.

First she saw a big hole in the ground. That surely wasn't safe. Children could trip and fall. Then she noticed that the inside edges of the slide were rough. That wasn't safe either. Clothes could get caught on a ride down. The ground was bare under the slide. A hard landing could hurt children. The bolts in the climbing dome stuck out, and they were rusty. A cut from rusty metal could be bad. A big slab of cement stuck out of the ground. It held the climbing dome in place. If children bumped into the slab, they could really get hurt. The seesaw was broken. It was dangerous to ride.

Patching A Playground

Devan and her friends painted the frame for the swings. On one side, they used green. On the other side, they used light brown. Afterward, each volunteer dipped a hand into the paint. They left green handprints on the light-brown side. They left light-brown handprints on the green side.

Devan thinks of these handprints as a way of saying: "we all worked hard together to make this playground safe."

Devan asked the 4-H Club to help keep this park in good shape. Now volunteers do just that. They are following Devan's example. If there's a playground that needs to be fixed, they know what to do.

◖ Volunteers help spread wood chips over the playground's surface. Wood chips make soft landing spots.

Devan was given a **budget** of $2,000 dollars to spend. She looked at a **catalog** of playground equipment. Each piece cost hundreds of dollars. She couldn't pick much.

Devan saw that the playground needed other work too. She asked members of her 4-H Club to help out.

☝ Devan chose two climbing bars to buy. Now both little and big kids had things to climb on.

© 2007 Macmillan/McGraw-Hill

Some Playground Safety Tips

Slide:
- Climb up the ladder one step at a time.
- Slide down in a sitting position, with feet forward.

Climbing Bars:
- Use only bars that you can reach.
- Never stand on bars or try to jump off.

Swings:
- There should be only one child per swing.
- Keep away from moving swings.

↻ It was unsafe to be on this seesaw.

CHAPTER 2

Can Devan Make a Plan?

Devan was troubled. Didn't her baby sister and other little children deserve a safe place to play?

Her mother said, "Well, you're the safety officer of your 4-H Club. What are you going to do?"

↻ This was another dangerous area in the playground.

↻ The barrel covered up the hole on the playground.

6

The committee also wanted Devan's advice. They asked what new equipment she thought the playground needed. Devan interviewed a mother at the playground. The mother spoke for other parents. They wanted swings with seats **designed** for little babies. Devan liked that idea. But she also thought about kids her age. There wasn't any equipment that they could use.

↻ Devan is happy and proud about the new equipment in her local playground.

Fast Fact

More children get hurt on climbing bars than on any other playground equipment.

11

© 2007 Macmillan/McGraw-Hill

CHAPTER 4

Where Did Devan Find Help?

With help from her mom, Devan used the Internet to find the details she needed for her list. She sent her report to the committee. In just a few days, their answer came. They said, "Yes."

Because of Devan's report, the committee had all the facts they needed. They were able to make some choices about how to make the playground safe.

☙ The committee fixed the seesaw so it was safe to use.

What Is a 4-H Club?

The 4-H Club is a national club for children. A four-leaf clover is its **symbol**. In each leaf is the letter H. The 4 *H*s stand for *Head*, *Heart*, *Hands*, and *Health*. Each club helps members to have fun, meet new people, learn life skills, build self-confidence, and learn to be responsible. Its slogan, or motto, is "To make the best better."

Devan made a photo tour of the playground by taking pictures of all of the dangerous areas.

What else could Devan do now? Devan was a responsible girl. She knew she had to do more. When she got home, she talked to her family. Then she got to work. She pasted the photos onto a presentation board. Later, with her family's help, Devan called Dave Schumm, the director of Bryan's parks. He set up a meeting.

CHAPTER 3

What Could Be Done?

Devan was very nervous. Would Mr. Schumm listen to her? Would he take her seriously? Devan was well prepared for the meeting. She showed Mr. Schumm her photos. And she told him what was wrong with the playground. When she was finished, Mr. Schumm told Devan she'd done a great job. Devan was thrilled.

Devan talks seriously to Mr. Schumm.

The swing set was in disrepair.

The slide had gaps in it which made it unsafe.

He did take her seriously after all. He even asked Devan for more help. He asked her to report her findings to a special **committee**. She needed to list exactly what needed to be fixed. If the committee members agreed with Devan's proposals, they would fix up the playground.

Word Workout

crate	determination	exact	luckiest
ruined	separate		storage

Moving Words Let's discuss these words. Then we can use them in a story about moving.

SPELLING WORDS

ponies	inches	flies	bunches	daisies
years	twins	cities	ashes	foxes
lunches	states	cherries	trays	alleys

One and Two I'll give you a word that names one thing. You can spell the word that means more than one.

(fold here)

© Macmillan/McGraw-Hill

Home-School Connection

Dear Family Member:

In *My Very Own Room*, a young girl is sharing a room with five brothers. What she wants more than anything is to have her own room. Because of the title, I think the girl will get her room in the end. I keep making predictions as I read. They are good guesses about what will happen next, and they're based on clues the author has given. Making predictions is fun—it's like solving little mysteries. The predictions also keep me involved in the story.

This Week's Skills

Comprehension: make and confirm predictions

Vocabulary: er and **est**

Spelling/Phonics: plurals

Name _____

What Might Happen?

Let's talk about each picture. What might happen next in a story about the picture? We can choose one picture and tell each other a short story about it and about our prediction.

Predictions

Predictions

Predictions

Predictions

Predictions

Predictions

Ejercicio de palabras

PALABRAS DE VOCABULARIO

crate	determination	exact	luckiest
ruined	separate		storage

Palabras de movimiento Discutimos estas palabras. Luego podemos usarlas en un cuento sobre mudarse.

PALABRAS DE ORTOGRAFÍA

ponies	inches	flies	bunches	daisies
years	twins	cities	ashes	foxes
lunches	states	cherries	trays	alleys

Uno y dos Te voy a dar una palabra que nombre una cosa. Deletrea la palabra en plural, o sea, más de uno.

(fold here)

Conexión con el hogar

Queridos familiares:

En *My Very Own Room*, una niña comparte una habitación con sus cinco hermanos. Lo que más quiere es tener su propia habitación. Por el título, supongo que la niña va a obtener su propia habitación al final del cuento. Sigo haciendo predicciones mientras leo. Son suposiciones de lo que va a pasar después y están basadas en pistas que el autor ha dado. Hacer predicciones es divertido porque es como resolver pequeños misterios. Las predicciones también mantienen el interés en el cuento.

Destrezas de la semana

Comprensión: hacer y confirmar predicciones

Vocabulario: er y est

Ortografía/Fonética: plurales

Nombre_____

¿Qué podría pasar?

Hablemos acerca de cada ilustración. ¿Qué podría pasar después en un cuento basado en una ilustración? Elijamos una ilustración y contémonos un cuento corto sobre la ilustración y nuestras predicciones.

Notes

Notes

Notes

Notes

Notes

Notes

Comprehension Check

Summarize

Review each chapter title. What predictions did you make about story events in each chapter? Were your predictions correct? Use your predictions to summarize the story.

What I Predict	What Happens

Think and Compare

1. Turn back to page 8. How did Julie's mother and the other parents probably feel once they heard about the blizzard? *(Make and Confirm Predictions)*

2. After reading the story, what do you think you would do if caught in a blizzard in the forest? *(Apply)*

3. The cell phone is a recent invention that can be helpful in emergencies. Discuss other situations in which a cell phone would be useful. *(Synthesize)*

16

A Winter Adventure

by Richard Brightfield
illustrated by Steve Attoe

Table of Contents

CHAPTER 1
Off They Go

"What are your plans for today?" Mr. Sanchez asked his son Carlo.

"I'm hiking with my nature club," Carlo said, "from the state park entrance to Turtle Lake. Jimmy's father, Mr. Gordon, is going with us."

"It's colder than yesterday," his mother said. "Please take your warmest jacket and your gloves."

© 2007 Macmillan/McGraw-Hill

A Winter Adventure

"Everybody jump on board," he said. "There's hot cider back at the gatehouse."

"Cool," said Carlo. "I think we're the luckiest kids alive."

When they got back to the gatehouse, Julie's and Tyrone's parents were waiting.

Everyone was safe and happy.

"It's all because of *Carlo's Igloo*," said Julie.

They all climbed out. Around them was a wonder-world of white.

"It's really beautiful!" Julie exclaimed.

A short time later, they heard the sound of a motor coming toward them. It was Carlo's father on a snowmobile. He was pulling an old-fashioned sleigh.

14

A Winter Adventure

"Hold on," Carlo's father said. "I need to get your warm blue jacket from the storage crate in the attic. Then I'll drop you off."

A short time later, Carlo met up with Mr. Gordon and the other members of the club, Jimmy, Julie, and Tyrone.

Mr. Gordon packed them in his van and drove them to the state park.

When they arrived he checked his compass. "The old logging trail is somewhere directly west of here," he said.

3

"This is it," Mr. Gordon said a short time later. "We'll follow the trail to the lake." They continued on into the pine forest. "Pine trees are my favorite," Mr. Gordon said. "They stay green all winter. Also, they saved the early settlers."

"How did they do that?" Tyrone asked.

"The Native Americans taught the settlers how to make pine-needle tea," Mr. Gordon said. "It kept the settlers from getting a disease called scurvy."

They had been hiking for an hour or so when Jimmy pointed excitedly ahead.

"Look! There's a roof, or something, fallen sideways on the trail!" he exclaimed. "Maybe the house got ruined in a storm."

CHAPTER 3

The Sleigh Ride

A while later, Mr. Gordon's phone rang. It was Carlo's father.

"I'm at the state park gatehouse," he said. "Where are you?"

"We're on the old logging trail a few miles due west of the gatehouse," Mr. Gordon said.

Luckily, Mr. Sanchez also had a compass. "Okay," he said. "I'm coming in to get you."

"Time to see what the outside world looks like," Mr. Gordon said.

"Great teamwork," said Mr. Gordon. "It's time to go in."

One by one they crawled into the igloo. Mr. Gordon had a flashlight. It lit up the inside. They sat with their backs against the wall.

"It's not the largest fort I've ever seen, but it's cozy," Mr. Gordon said. "We'll wait out the blizzard."

"This is great," Julie said. "We'll call it *Carlo's Igloo* because it was his idea to build it."

12

A Winter Adventure

5

Mr. Gordon laughed. "That's a lean-to," he said. "We'll stop there to rest."

They all sat on a bench in front of the lean-to.

"This is probably the simplest structure known to man," Mr. Gordon said. "It's a good shelter during a summer storm. It doesn't give much protection in the winter though."

Just then a gust of wind blew by.

"Whoa. It's getting colder," said Tyrone.

6

A Winter Adventure

11

"We'll get started," she said.

"We have to leave a small opening on one side," Carlo said as he started building.

Mr. Gordon went toward the nearest tree and cut off some of the lowest branches with his hunting knife. He separated them into two bunches and then carried each bunch to the rapidly rising snow fort. When Julie said it was high enough, he and Tyrone started laying the branches across the top. They were determined to make a perfect roof.

10

A Winter Adventure

"Yes," said Carlo. "It's colder now than before. Look up! The clouds have covered the sun."

"We still have a long way to go," said Mr. Gordon. "We will keep warm by walking."

They started on the trail again. A few snowflakes began to fall.

"It's snowing," Jimmy said. "Maybe we should start back."

"It's just a flurry," said Tyrone.

But a few minutes later, the snow began coming down heavily.

7

CHAPTER 2
The Big Blizzard

"I think it's time for me to make a phone call," Mr. Gordon said. He took out his cell phone and called Julie's mother. "It's snowing up here," he said. "This blizzard is a surprise. I listened to a weather report, but didn't hear anything about an upcoming storm."

"I'll let the other parents know," she said.

Mr. Gordon could barely hear her. "Don't worry, we'll be fine!" he shouted into the phone.

The snow started coming down so hard that they could barely see the trail or even the trees. It was a real blizzard.

"We need to find some shelter," Julie said.

A Winter Adventure

"Let's build an igloo," said Carlo. "I read about building one in a book."

"That sounds like a good idea," Mr. Gordon said.

Mr. Gordon pulled a tape measure from his pack and handed it to Julie. "I'll put you in charge of the measurements," he said. "The wall of the fort should be circular, about six feet across and three feet high. Make it a foot and a half thick. The measurements don't have to be exact, but should be close."

Word Workout

© Macmillan/McGraw-Hill

(fold here)

Home-School Connection

Dear Family Member:

I'm reading the story *Boom Town*, which tells about a young girl and her family who moved west. Amanda is bored, and so she bakes a pie. After people begin buying her pies, Amanda starts a bakery. Things happen one after another. I keep track of the things that happen and the order, or sequence, in which they happen. When I finish reading, I'll know which events are really important. I guess they'll lead me to know how *Boom Town* came to be.

This Week's Skills

Comprehension: sequence

Vocabulary: word parts

Spelling/Phonics: compound words

Name _____

Sequence Scramble

Tallulah is having a busy day. Let's look at her list of things to do. Can we put them in the correct sequence?

- Piano lesson at 4:00.

- Drop off Rob's book after seeing Gina.

- Watch the TV movie with Sis tonight.

- Meet Gina for lunch.

- Help cook dinner.

- Remember to bring Rob's book with me this morning.

Plan Your Perfect Day

Think about what would happen if you could plan a perfect day. Tell what you would do, who you would see, and what you might eat. Put the events in order. What would happen first? next? last?

Ejercicio de palabras

PALABRAS DE VOCABULARIO

blossomed	grumbled	lonesome
sidewalks	traders	wailed

El viejo Oeste Pensemos acerca de un lugar en el viejo Oeste que está comenzando a convertirse en un pueblo. Podemos usar las palabras de arriba para narrar un relato corto.

PALABRAS DE ORTOGRAFÍA

birdhouse	airplane	basketball	someone
sometime	newspaper	sidewalks	notebook
hairdo	birthday	barefoot	stagecoach
headlight	daylight	daytime	

Doble trabajo Te voy a dar la mitad de una palabra compuesta. Puedes decirme la otra mitad y luego deletrear la palabra completa. ¿Quieres invertir papeles y darme la mitad de cada palabra?

Conexión con el hogar

Queridos familiares:

Estoy leyendo el cuento *Boom Town,* sobre una niña y su familia que se mudaron al Oeste. Como Amanda está aburrida, entonces hornea un pastel. Después de personas empieza de comprar sus pasteles, Amanda abre una pastelería. Las cosas ocurren una después de otra. Sigo el orden de las cosas que ocurren y el orden, o sequencia, en que ocurren. Cuando termine de leer, sabré qué sucesos son realmente importantes. Supongo que los sucesos me dejarán saber cómo surgió *Boom Town.*

Destrezas de la semana

Comprensión: orden de los sucesos

Vocabulario: partes de una palabra

Ortografía/Fonética: palabras compuestas

Nombre _____

Secuencia desordenada

Tallulah tiene un día ocupado. Observemos su lista de cosas para hacer. ¿Podemos ordenar las cosas en el orden correcto?

- Piano lesson at 4:00.

- Drop off Rob's book after seeing Gina.

- Watch the TV movie with Sis tonight.

- Meet Gina for lunch.

- Help cook dinner.

- Remember to bring Rob's book with me this morning.

Planea tu día perfecto

Piensa acerca de lo que ocurriría si pudieras planear un día perfecto. Di lo que harías, a quién verías y qué comerías. Coloca los sucesos en orden. ¿Qué ocurriría primero? ¿Después? ¿Y por último?

Comprehension Check

Summarize

Use a Sequence Chart to tell about the jobs that frontier children did on farms. Then use the chart to help summarze what you learned.

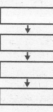

Think and Compare

1. Look back at pages 10–11. Explain when the Pony Express started and what the riders did. Use words such as *first, second, then, next, finally.* **(Identify Sequence of Events)**

2. If you were a frontier child would you prefer to work on a farm, in a town, on a steamboat, or for the Pony Express? Explain your choice. **(Synthesize)**

3. How is the work frontier children did like that of children's work today? How is it different? **(Evaluate: Compare and Contrast)**

CHILDREN AT WORK: On the Frontier

by Truman Vega

Table of Contents

⟫ Introduction ⟪

They came by horse and wagon. They came by flatboat down rivers. They came with everything they owned. Most made the trip west with their parents. Some came alone.

From the 1780s to the 1880s, thousands of children moved to the **frontier**. They started a new life at the western edge of settled land in the United States.

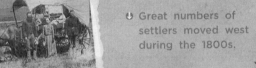

↻ Great numbers of settlers moved west during the 1800s.

Areas settled by:
- 1810
- 1830
- 1850
- 1870
- 1890
- 1900

PACIFIC OCEAN

Gulf of Mexico

ATLANTIC OCEAN

Glossary

barter *(BAHR-tuhr)* to trade by exchanging goods or services *(page 4)*

frontier *(frun-TEER)* land along the edge of a settled area *(page 2)*

harvest *(HAHR-vist)* the gathering in of a crop when it is ripe *(page 6)*

orphan *(AWR-fuhn)* a child whose parents have died *(page 12)*

plains *(PLAYNZ)* grasslands in the Middle West states used mostly for raising cattle and wheat; also called Great Plains *(page 4)*

telegraph *(TEL-i-graf)* a machine for sending and receiving messages *(page 11)*

Index

❧ Conclusion ❧

Life on the frontier was often hard for young children and teens. They did what they could to help their families. They worked on farms and in towns. They worked on boats and on the dusty roads. And they earned money whenever they could.

◔ Many pioneer boys took care of the animals.

◔ These are some important dates in frontier history.

Frontier Time Line

- **1803**
  Louisiana Purchase doubles size of the United States

- **1848**
  Gold Rush begins

- **1862**
  Homestead Act

1803 ——————————————— 1890

- **1860**
  The Pony Express begins

- **1890**
  End of western frontier

◔ Pioneer children did all kinds of chores.

Families moved west for many reasons. Some wanted their own land to start a new life. Others wanted to find gold. Still others came for adventure.

In 1862 the Homestead Act made moving to the frontier possible for these families. They paid the government $18 for 160 acres of land. To keep the land, the family had to build a house on it. Then they had to live in it for at least five years.

CHAPTER 1
⇒ On the Farm ⇐

The early farmers had little need for money. They mostly **bartered**. They traded one kind of work for another. One farmer might help a neighbor build a barn. The neighbor, in turn, might train horses.

Farming on the **plains** was hard work. Most families were large. Children were put to work at an early age.

↻ These pioneers settled in Nebraska. They built a sod house.

4

Boys also worked as cabin boys on steamboats. Their job was to serve the captain, the crew, and riders. It was also a way to see the country.

Girls sometimes were hired to do "boys' work." A telegraph company in Utah Territory trained a few teenage girls. The girls learned quickly and earned money running the telegraph.

↻ Steamboats were a popular way to travel before the age of railroads.

13

CHAPTER 4
❧ Alone ❧

Not all frontier children lived with parents. Some were **orphans** from the East. They came west on "orphan trains" that charities set up. These children must have been lonesome, but they wanted to find jobs and better their lives.

Some young boys got jobs at general stores. This kind of store was an interesting and busy place. It served as the town's post office and meeting place. People could buy most of the goods they needed.

ON SALE AT THE GENERAL STORE

- blades for scythes and sickles
- baskets of seeds
- saddles, bridles, and harnesses
- flour, sugar, salt
- cloth, dye, clothing

© 2007 Macmillan/McGraw-Hill

GIRLS AT WORK

Girls learned to do many types of handiwork. They made samplers. They made rugs with rags. They even wove blankets.

They carried water from streams or wells. They gathered wood to be used as fuel for stoves or fireplaces. They also milked cows and took care of the farm animals.

Sometimes girls and boys had different chores. Girls helped around the house. They looked after the younger children. They helped clean and cook. They made soap and candles and gathered eggs.

During spring and summer, girls worked in the garden. They preserved fruits and vegetables for the long winter ahead. While the snow blew and the winds wailed, the girls sat near the fire and sewed.

WHAT ABOUT SCHOOL?

Work came first, school second. If farm children went to school at all, it was in winter when they had fewer chores.

The boys' work often followed the seasons too. In spring they helped plow the land and plant crops. In summer and early fall, they **harvested** the crops. They learned how to cut hay. They hunted when they could. Some of them tamed horses or herded cattle.

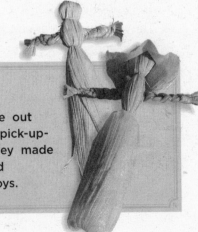

FAST FACT

Children did take time out for fun. They played pick-up-sticks with straws. They made cornhusk dolls, carved whistles, and other toys.

6

© 2007 Macmillan/McGraw-Hill

The answer was the Pony Express. The Pony Express started in April of 1860. A rider earned $100 a month. One rider with a pack of letters would ride for miles to a certain area. He would then change horses and travel on to a pony express station. Another rider would be waiting there. He would take the mail and ride another stretch. This went on and on, with one rider after another, until the letters finally reached their destination.

In the fall of 1861, use of the **telegraph** began. It was a much faster and cheaper way to send messages.

PONY EXPRESS !

CHANGE OF TIME!   REDUCED RATES!

10 Days to San Francisco!

LETTERS

WILL BE RECEIVED AT THE

OFFICE, 84 BROADWAY,

NEW YORK,

Up to **4** P. M. every TUESDAY,

AND

Up to **2½** P. M. every SATURDAY,

Which will be forwarded to connect with the PONY EXPRESS leaving ST. JOSEPH, Missouri,

Every **WEDNESDAY** and **SATURDAY** at II P. M.

TELEGRAMS

Sent to Fort Kearney on the mornings of MONDAY and FRIDAY, will connect with PONY leaving St. Joseph, WEDNESDAYS and SATURDAYS.

EXPRESS CHARGES.

LETTERS weighing half ounce or under................$1 00
For every additional half ounce or fraction of an ounce 1 00
In all cases to be enclosed in 10 cent Government Stamped Envelopes,
And all Express CHARGES Pre-paid.

☞ PONY EXPRESS ENVELOPES For Sale at our Office.

WELLS, FARGO & CO., Ag'ts.

New York, July 1, 1861.

SLOTE & JANES, STATIONERS AND PRINTERS, 8 FULTON STREET, NEW YORK

⌐ This poster was put up in post offices and country stores.

11

© 2007 Macmillan/McGraw-Hill

CHAPTER 3
❖ The Riders ❖

Mail service in the mid-1800s was slow. Letters traveled by ship from the East Coast around the tip of South America to the West Coast. This could take months.

How could the mail be delivered faster?

↻ A Pony Express rider had to weigh less than 125 pounds.

↻ Pony Express riders carried the mail between Missouri and California.

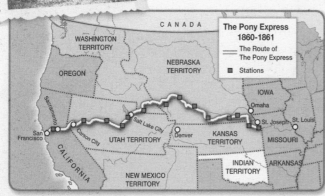

The Pony Express 1860-1861
— The Route of The Pony Express
■ Stations

10

CHAPTER 2
❖ In Town ❖

Life in towns was different from life on the farms. Towns grew for different reasons. Some began as trading posts. Others were near water where people could make a living fishing. Some towns grew because the forest provided work for loggers.

Mining towns developed after the gold rush began in 1848. Children helped the gold miners by cleaning the equipment the men used in their work. The children also looked for their own gold.

This gold miner ↻ went to California to pan for gold.

7

A small mining town had a few shops lining a dirt street with no sidewalk. Traders came to town with goods from the East. Miners went into town for the tools and food they needed.

In town children had a chance to make money. They sold newspapers and baked bread. They sold flowers and food from their gardens.

☝ If miners stopped finding gold nearby, people often left a town forever. It became a "ghost town."

☞ Many children in the West delivered items, such as coal and lamp oil.

Other towns blossomed in the West, too. Children did chores for shopkeepers. This work was not always fun. The children didn't grumble about it, especially if they got paid.

Boys had more job choices than girls. Older boys could help print the town newspaper. They could work for a blacksmith and learn how to make tools and horseshoes. Some could even drive a stagecoach from one town to another.

Word Workout

WORDS TO KNOW

gift   kindhearted   sturdy   tend

produce   schoolhouse   yearned

Because, That's Why! Let's take each word and use it in one or two sentences that tell about a cause or an effect.

SPELLING WORDS

names   named   naming   hopes

hoped   hoping   dances   danced

dancing   drops   dropped   dropping

wraps   wrapped   wrapping

How Many Ways Take a good look at your spelling words. I'll give you the base word, the word from which all others stem. Tell me the spelling word with endings **s, ed,** or **ing.**

(fold here)

Home-School Connection

Dear Family Member:

We're reading the story *Beatrice's Goat.* A girl named Beatrice longs to go to school, but her family does not have the money to send her. Then her family is given a goat. The goat gives birth, and Beatrice begins to sell her goat's milk. Then Beatrice gets money. It's easy to see that one thing leads to another in this story. I bet that in the end something else will happen, and Beatrice will go to school.

This Week's Skills

Comprehension: cause and effect

Vocabulary: word families

Spelling/Phonics: adding **s, ed,** and **ing**

Name _____

What's Happening?

We can read the sentences and look at the pictures. Let's talk about them. See if we can think of what *might* happen because of what *is* happening. We can come up with many effects for each picture.

Ellen's mom gave her five dollars.

Kayla caught the flu.

What's Happening?

Raul's dog won first prize in the dog tricks contest.

Kayla has wonderful photographs.

Ejercicio de palabras

PALABRAS DE VOCABULARIO

gift	kindhearted	sturdy	tend
produce	schoolhouse	yearned	

¡Es por eso! Vamos a tomar cada palabra y usarla en una o dos oraciones que nos cuenten una causa o un efecto.

PALABRAS DE ORTOGRAFÍA

names	named	naming	hopes
hoped	hoping	dances	danced
dancing	drops	dropped	dropping
wraps	wrapped	wrapping	

¿Cuántas maneras? Observa bien tus palabras de ortografía. Te voy a dar la palabra base, la palabra de la cual todas las otras se derivan. Dime la palabra de ortografía que tenga las terminaciones **s, ed** o **ing**.

© Macmillan/McGraw-Hill ···· (fold here) ····

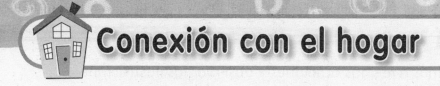

Conexión con el hogar

Queridos familiares:

Estamos leyendo el cuento *Beatrice's Goat*. Una niña que se llama Beatrice anhela ir a la escuela, pero su familia no tiene dinero para enviarla. Después, su familia recibe una cabra. La cabra da a luz cabritos y Beatrice comienza a vender la leche de la cabra. Entonces Beatrice consigue dinero. Es fácil ver en este cuento que una cosa lleva a otra. Apuesto a que al final otra cosa va a ocurrir y Beatrice va a poder ir a la escuela.

Destrezas de la semana

Comprensión: causa y efecto

Vocabulario: familia de palabras

Ortografía/Fonética: añadir **s, ed** y **ing**

Nombre _____

¿Qué está ocurriendo?

Vamos a leer las oraciones y observar las ilustraciones. Hablemos acerca de ellas. Veamos si podemos pensar en lo que *podría* ocurrir debido a lo que *está* ocurriendo. Cada ilustración podría tener varios efectos.

Ellen's mom gave her five dollars.

Kayla caught the flu.

¿Qué está ocurriendo?

Raul's dog won first prize in the dog tricks contest.

Kayla has wonderful photographs.

Comprehension Check

Summarize

Use a Cause and Effect Chart to record causes and effects from the book. Then use the information to summarize the book.

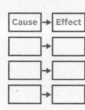

Think and Compare

1. Turn back to page 6. What causes mountain valleys to form? *(Identify Cause and Effect)*

2. What kinds of hikes or nature walks have you taken? What did you see and do on the trails? *(Apply)*

3. A trail and a glacier have been named to honor Muir. What other ways do people honor others for their good deeds? Can you suggest a new way to honor people? *(Evaluate)*

John Muir
Friend of Nature
BY RICHARD BRIGHTFIELD

Table of Contents

Introduction

Yosemite **National** Park in California is one of the most beautiful places in the United States. It has rugged mountains and high waterfalls with their bases wrapped in rainbows.

There are trails for hiking, grounds for camping, and fast-flowing waters for river rafting.

The coyotes howl and the birds sing while bears and deer walk among the trees.

One man who came to the United States as a boy helped to save Yosemite's natural wonders for you to enjoy. His name was John Muir.

Coyotes can be ⤴ found in Yosemite.

© 2007 Macmillan/McGraw-Hill

Glossary

botany (*BOT-uh-nee*) the study of plants *(page 6)*

erosion (*i-ROH-zhuhn*) a wearing, washing, or eating away of something, such as rock and soil *(page 6)*

geology (*jee-OL-uh-jee*) the science that deals with the study of the earth *(page 6)*

glacier (*GLAY-shuhr*) a huge piece of ice in very cold areas *(page 6)*

national (*NASH-uh-nuhl*) having to do with our country united under one government *(page 2)*

Index

Conclusion

The Grand Canyon of the Colorado River was one of Muir's favorite places. He traveled there often. He would stand and look as the colors changed throughout the day. The pale blues, pinks, and whites turned to silver and gold as the sun set on this huge canyon.

Muir died in 1914. After his death, people honored him. A mountain trail in Yosemite is named after him. It is called the *Muir Trail*. If you visit Yosemite, you might see it.

↻ People enjoy the Muir Trail year after year.

14

© 2007 Macmillan/McGraw-Hill

John Muir: Friend of Nature

↻ People enjoy all kinds of activities in Yosemite National Park.

↻ The Vernal Falls in Yosemite National Park is a wonderful sight.

3

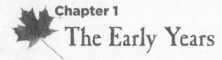

Chapter 1
The Early Years

John Muir was born in a small town in Scotland in 1838. His family moved to the United States when he was eleven. They moved to what is now Wisconsin and set up a farm there. They were pioneers.

Muir went to school in a small schoolhouse. He liked being a schoolboy. The rest of the time he worked on the farm. He was busy from sunup until sundown. But Muir yearned for more. He knew he didn't want to tend the farm all his life. Muir liked to read and he read often. He also liked to invent things. He made a special thermometer. And he made something he called his "early-rising machine."

Muir once said:

" *It's always sunrise somewhere.* "

John Muir: Friend of Nature

The Grand Canyon is another beautiful national park.

The Sierra Club

Muir and his friends founded the Sierra Club to "protect the land, forests, and watersheds of the Sierra Nevada Mountains." Muir was its first president. The club still works to help protect our wildlife.

John Muir's efforts to protect nature helped lead to the founding of the National Park Service. This organization helps to protect and preserve the natural wonders of this country.

Some National Parks from Largest to Smallest		
Park	State	Size in Acres
Yellowstone	Idaho, Montana, Wyoming	2,218,823
Everglades	Florida	1,398,800
Yosemite	California	760,917
Carlsbad Caverns	New Mexico	46,755

© 2007 Macmillan/McGraw-Hill

Muir brought his invention to a state fair like this one.

This machine was sort of an early alarm clock. At a set time, the bed would tip and toss the sleeper out of bed.

Muir took his machine to the state fair to exhibit it. A long line of boys lined up for a separate turn on the machine. Each would lie down and pretend to be asleep. Then the bed would tilt and toss the boy out of bed. Muir's early-rising machine was a big hit!

Muir won a prize and made front-page news. Soon he was offered a number of jobs. Instead he left for college.

In college Muir studied both **geology** and **botany**.

Muir's geology teacher taught that many mountain valleys had been carved out by **glaciers**. Few people believed this at the time. Muir studied glaciers and helped to prove that his teacher was right.

Muir wanted to study in the wild. First he went to Canada and hiked through the wilderness there. He wrote in his journal and took samples of plants.

What Does a Geologist Study?

Geologists study rocks and earth. They want to know how the forces of nature, like earthquakes and erosion, formed the landscape.

© 2007 Macmillan/McGraw-Hill

⌒ Redwoods in Sequoia National Park

In 1906 a law was passed that allowed a president to save places of historic importance. Teddy Roosevelt used this law to create 18 such places. They included the Grand Canyon, the Petrified Forest, and the Great Sequoias.

Chapter 3
Making a Difference

Muir was lucky. He found someone who would help him save Yosemite and other great places. This person was none other than Theodore Roosevelt, the President of the United States.

Roosevelt read Muir's articles. The two became friends. Roosevelt became a big supporter of Muir's goal to protect nature.

President Theodore ↻ Roosevelt and Muir enjoy Yosemite's beauty.

What Does a Botanist Study?

Botanists study plants. They learn where plants live and how they grow.

Later, in the United States, he walked a thousand miles from Kentucky to the Gulf of Mexico. On the trip Muir became very ill. Luckily his kindhearted family sent him a gift of money. With it he went to California. Once he got there, his health improved.

↻ This is the Muir Glacier in Alaska. It is named to honor John Muir.

John Muir's 1000 mile walk to the Gulf of Mexico
— John Muir's route

ILLINOIS INDIANA OHIO W. VIR.
Louisville
Elizabethtown KENTUCKY VIRGINIA
Glasgow
Jamestown
TENNESSEE Murphy Philadelphia NORTH CAROLINA
ARKANSAS Athens SOUTH CAROLINA
MISSISSIPPI Thomson
ALABAMA Savannah ATLANTIC OCEAN
TEXAS GEORGIA
LOUISIANA Gainesville Fernandina
FLORIDA 0 200 miles
Gulf of Mexico Cedar Keys

Chapter 2
On the Trails

So again Muir took off for the mountains. After a while, he reached Yosemite in California.

Muir fell in love with this spectacular place. Its natural wonders awed him.

Muir hoped to preserve the beauty of areas like Yosemite. He wanted them to stay just as they were. He wanted to keep people from building on them.

Yosemite National Park

Yosemite National Park covers about 760,000 acres of eastern California. It is named after the Yosemite nation of Native Americans who once lived there. Over 60 kinds of animals, 200 kinds of birds, and 1,300 kinds of plants live in Yosemite. It has some of the highest waterfalls in the world.

This is a view of the ➔ Yosemite National Park from Glacier Point.

8

Muir began writing magazine articles about the dangers that could hurt Yosemite. He wrote about many other beautiful places in the United States. People were chopping down the sturdy trees to produce roof shingles. Sheep and cows were eating all the plants. Muir wanted to protect natural places.

☉ Cathedral Rocks

☉ El Capitan

9

Word Workout

(fold here)

WORDS TO KNOW

artist's declared existed

powered pride

I Think Let's try to make up opinions about things, using the words above.

SPELLING WORDS

tries tried trying dries dried

drying hurries hurried hurrying studies

studied studying plays played playing

Y Am I Happy? I'm going to write down the base words of these spelling words: *try, dry, hurry, study,* and *play.* Then I'll ask you to spell the words adding **s, ed,** and **ing.** Can you do it? You can turn the table and ask me to add the endings.

Home-School Connection

Dear Family Member:

We're reading "A Carousel of Dreams." It's an article about carousels. The writer says that one carousel is the most fantastic in the nation. That's just his opinion—it can't be proved. There are facts, too. For a park in New York City, kids' drawings were used to make the animals on the carousel.

This Week's Skills

Comprehension: fact and opinion

Vocabulary: possessives, such as *the boy's bike*

Spelling/Phonics: words which change **y** to **i,** such as *cherry* to *cherries*

Name _____

Facts and Opinions

You get your information from many different sources—television, computers, books, newspapers, and people, too! Let's look at each information source below. We'll try to think of a fact and an opinion that could come from each one.

a magazine

a newspaper

an ad about cars on television

sportsheroes.com

Ejercicio de palabras

PALABRAS DE VOCABULARIO

artist's declared existed

powered pride

Yo pienso Intentemos formar opiniones acerca de algunas cosas, usando las palabras de arriba.

PALABRAS DE ORTOGRAFÍA

tries   tried   trying   dries   dried

drying   hurries   hurried   hurrying   studies

studied   studying   plays   played   playing

¿Por qué estoy feliz? Voy a escribir las palabras base de estas palabras de ortografía: *try, dry, hurry, study* y *play*. Luego, te voy a pedir que deletrees las palabras agregando las terminaciones **s, ed** y **ing**. ¿Puedes hacerlo? Puedes invertir papeles conmigo y pedirme que yo agregue las terminaciones.

Conexión con el hogar

Queridos familiares:

Estamos leyendo *A Carousel of Dreams*. Es un artículo acerca de los carruseles. El escritor dice que un carrusel en especial es el más fantástico de la nación. Eso es sólo una opinion ya que no se puede comprobar. También hay hechos. Para un parque en la ciudad de Nueva York fueron usados dibujos de niños para hacer los animales en el carrusel.

Destrezas de la semana

Comprensión: hecho y opinión

Vocabulario: posesivos como *the boy's bike*

Ortografía/Fonética: palabras que cambian **y** por **i**, como *cherry* a *cherries*

Nombre_____

© Macmillan/McGraw-Hill · · · · · (fold here)

273

Hechos y opiniones

Tú obtienes información de muchas fuentes diferentes, por ejemplo, de la televisión, la computadora, los libros, los periódicos y también de la gente. Observemos cada fuente de información aquí abajo. Intentaremos pensar en un hecho y en una opinión que podría provenir de cada fuente.

A magazine

A newspaper

A show about cars on television.

sportsheroes.com

Comprehension Check

Summarize

List the facts and opinions found in this book. Remember, a fact is something that can be proven. Use your list to summarize the information in the book.

Think and Compare

1. Look at page 7. Name one opinion that is expressed. Name one fact that is stated. *(Evaluate Fact and Opinion)*

2. Which roller coaster would you most like to ride? Why? *(Apply)*

3. Why are roller coasters popular all over the world? *(Evaluate)*

Thrills and Chills

by Michele Spirn

Table of Contents

Introduction

You grab onto the cold metal bar. You ride up to the highest point. You feel like something is pushing you backwards. You get to the top and stare down. You gasp. It's a big drop. Your stomach twists and turns. There's no time to think about it.

Thrills and Chills

Glossary

air pressure *(AYR PRESH-uhr)* the force that air puts on things *(page 12)*

balance *(BAL-uhns)* the condition in which opposite sides or parts are the same weight, amount, or force *(page 11)*

energy *(EN-uhrj-ee)* the capacity for doing work or supplying power *(page 10)*

gravity *(GRAV-i-tee)* the force that pulls things toward the center of the earth *(page 11)*

kinetic *(kuh-NE-tik)* having to do with motion *(page 10)*

track *(TRAK)* a set of rails on which trains move *(page 10)*

Index

Conclusion

Roller coasters have existed for hundreds of years. People enjoy getting chills and thrills from riding them. Next time you ride one, think about what roller coasters were like long ago. Think about the kinds of energy they use. Think about how slow they once were compared to how fast they are today. Roller coasters are one great ride.

Roller coasters like⟳ these are popular rides in amusement parks.

Down, down, down you go, screaming all the way. Your heart is still beating as you glide to a stop. You smile. You made it! Now it's time to get off the roller coaster.

Do you know who invented the roller coaster? Did you ever wonder how it works? How does a roller coaster stay on its tracks and not fly off?

↻ People of all ages enjoy riding roller coasters.

Thrills and Chills

3

CHAPTER 1

How Did Roller Coasters Begin?

Around the time the Pilgrims were landing in the New World, the Russians were building the first roller coaster. They built huge wooden slides. Then they poured water on them. In the cold winter, the water turned to ice. Large sleds would race down these icy slides.

↻ People in Russia enjoyed their huge slides.

4

Staying Safe On a Roller Coaster

Follow these rules for fun and safety.

* Always follow the rules on the signs.
* Always listen to the person in charge.
* Never throw anything from the roller coaster.
* If you see someone doing something dangerous, report it.
* Never take off your seat belt or lap bar during the ride.
* Stay seated until you are told you can get off the ride.

13

Riding a roller coaster can be scary. Sometimes it feels as if the roller coaster might fly off the track. Why doesn't this happen? Each roller coaster car has three sets of wheels. One set of safety wheels locks onto the track. These wheels grip the rail. The car can't fly off. The roller coaster also has a safety brake that is powered by **air pressure**.

People who run amusement parks pride themselves on making sure their roller coasters are in good shape. Workers check them every day. In the winter, most roller coasters are taken apart. Broken parts are fixed. Then the roller coasters are put together again.

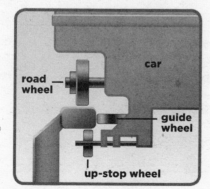

This diagram shows ↩ the different kinds of wheels on a roller coaster.

road wheel

car

guide wheel

up-stop wheel

© 2007 Macmillan/McGraw-Hill

Catherine II (1729-1796) was ↩ a German princess before she became Empress of Russia.

Over one hundred years later, Empress Catherine the Great of Russia asked workmen to build her a special slide. She wanted one that could be used in the summer. In 1784, they built one that could be ridden on by a cart on wheels. Many people think this was the first real roller coaster.

An artist painted Empress Catherine's slide. People said that the artist's work was fit for a queen.

The first American roller coaster was built in the mountains of Pennsylvania. It was called the Mauch Chunk Switchback Railway. It was more like a train than a roller coaster. When it was first built in 1827, it was used to carry coal. Then, in 1873, people began riding the train for fun.

↻ The railway carried 35,000 people a year down 2,322 feet (708 m) of track. Riders had a great view of the surrounding river and mountains.

© 2007 Macmillan/McGraw-Hill

Gravity, the pull between the coaster and the earth, also drags the coaster down the hill.

In 1938 a famous scientist, Albert Einstein, found that no hill on a roller coaster could be higher than the first hill, the lift hill. If any of the other hills were higher, the energy would not be **balanced**.

Most roller coasters will lose speed at the end of the ride because friction builds up. Friction is the rubbing of the wheels against the track. This rubbing causes the roller coaster to slow down.

Did You Know . . .
The word *energy* comes from a Greek word that means "activity."

↺ A baseball player uses both potential and kinetic energy to throw a ball.

CHAPTER 2

How Do Roller Coasters Work?

How does a roller coaster work? An engine does not power it. The first car has a bar underneath. A moving chain catches onto this bar and drags the coaster up the hill.

Energy is stored in the car from the pull up the hill. That's potential energy. When the ride starts down the hill, the stored energy drives the coaster. It moves with **kinetic** energy along the **track**.

This is a diagram of a roller coaster ride.

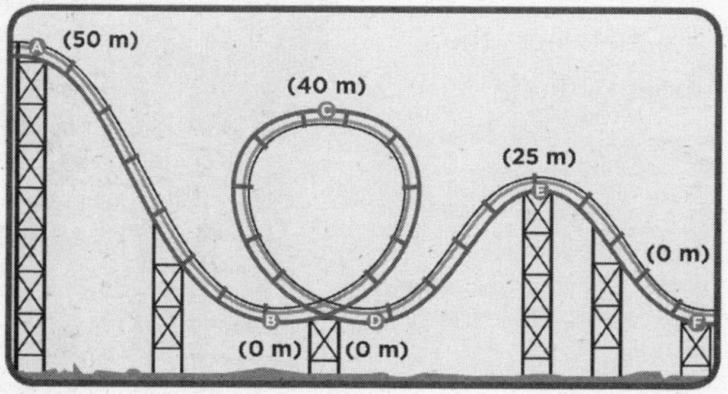

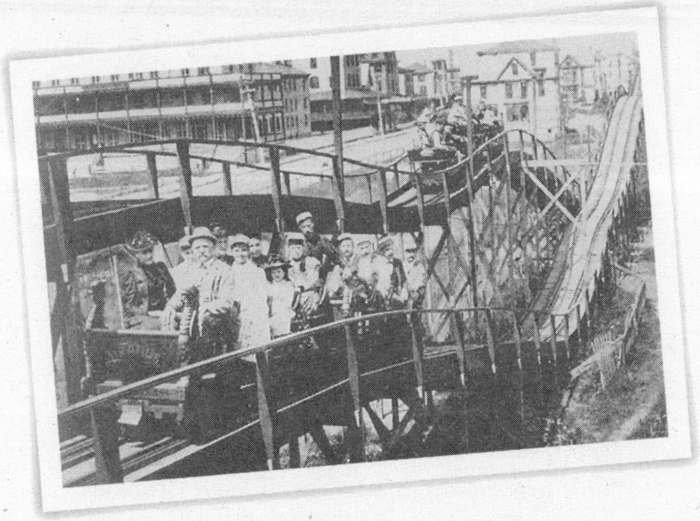

Some riders sat sideways in Thompson's roller coaster. This gave them a better view.

In 1884 another roller coaster was invented. It rolled six miles an hour (9.6 k/h) down a track 650 feet (198 m) long. This is about the speed of a very fast bicycle ride. In those days, people who rode it felt like they were racing.

This roller coaster was in an amusement park in Coney Island, New York. It cost one nickel to ride it. It was invented by LaMarcus Adna Thompson.

Today, there are about 1,850 roller coasters around the world. North America has over 700.

Roller coasters keep getting bigger. In 2003 an amusement park in Ohio declared it had the world's tallest and fastest roller coaster. It is called the Top Thrill Dragster. By the time you read this an even bigger and faster roller coaster may exist. Plans are being made for a new "rocket coaster," 456 feet (139 m) high and able to run 128 miles per hour (206 k/h).

Fastest Roller Coasters		
Roller Coaster	**Speed**	**Location**
Top Thrill Dragster	120 mph (193 k/h)	Cedar Point Sandusky, Ohio
Dodonpa	106.8 mph (172 k/h)	Fujikyu Highland Fuji-Yosida, Japan
Steel Dragon 2000	95 mph (153 k/h)	Nagashima Spa Land, Japan
Millennium Force	92 mph (148 k/h)	Cedar Point Sandusky, Ohio
Goliath	85 mph (137 k/h)	Six Flags Magic Mountain, Valencia, California

Built for Fun

In 1894, Paul Boynton opened the first modern amusement park in Chicago. It had the first loop-the-loop roller coaster.

⊕ Modern-day loop-the-loop.

Japan's Dodonpa is an unusual roller coaster. Each car has a face painted on it. The mouth on each face is open. It looks like the face is screaming. The seats are between the mouth's teeth.

On the Dodonpa ⟳ roller coaster, you speed down a 156-foot (47.5 m) drop.

Word Workout

WORDS TO KNOW

escape screamed image newspaper

numb shuddered fled

Story Time Let's make up a story about getting out of a fire safely. We'll use the words above.

SPELLING WORDS

invite	napkin	follow	Sunday
basket	chapter	number	fellow
butter	mammal	letter	chicken
bedtime	problem	rabbit	

Your Turn Now It's your turn to test my spelling. Ask me to spell each word. If I misspell a word, tell me how to spell it correctly. When we're done, I'll give you the words to spell.

·······(fold here)·······

Home-School Connection

Dear Family Member:

The Printer is a story about a man who is deaf. He is a printer. Although he knows how to talk with his hands, the other printers do not know sign language. One day a fire begins back in a corner, and the man does not know how to tell anyone. The man is intelligent and caring, so I'm predicting he will find a way to get everyone to safety. As I keep reading, I'll find out if I'm right.

This Week's Skills

Comprehension: make and confirm predictions

Vocabulary Strategy: context clues

Spelling/Phonics: syllables

Name _____

Coin Toss

We're going to toss a coin ten times. Before we begin, however, we're going to predict how many times it will land heads and how many times it will land tails. We can write our prediction below. Each time the coin lands, we'll make a mark on the tally sheet to the right. In math, this exercise is called a probability problem.

Our Prediction

We think the coin will land heads _____ times.

We think the coin will land tails _____ times.

	HEADS	TAILS
1st toss		
2nd toss		
3rd toss		
4th toss		
5th toss		
6th toss		
7th toss		
8th toss		
9th toss		
10th toss		

The Results

The coin landed heads _____ times.

The coin landed tails _____ times.

Was our prediction correct? _____

Ejercicio de palabras

PALABRAS DE VOCABULARIO

escape	screamed	image	newspaper
numb	shuddered	fled	

Tiempo de cuentos Inventemos un cuento acerca de escapar a salvo de un incendio. Vamos a usar las palabras de arriba.

PALABRAS DE ORTOGRAFÍA

invite	napkin	follow	Sunday
basket	chapter	number	fellow
butter	mammal	letter	chicken
bedtime	problem	rabbit	

Ahora es tu turno Ahora es tu turno para poner a prueba mi ortografía. Pídeme que deletree cada palabra. Si deletreo una palabra en forma incorrecta, dime cómo hacerlo correctamente. Cuando terminemos, yo te daré las palabras para deletrear.

© Macmillan/McGraw-Hill

·····(fold here)·····

Conexión con el hogar

Queridos familiares:

The Printer es un cuento acerca de un hombre que es sordo. Él es un tipógrafo. Si bien él sabe cómo hablar por señas con sus manos, los otros tipógrafos no conocen el lenguaje por señas. Un día comienza un incendio en una esquina y el hombre no sabe cómo avisarles a las otras personas. Como el hombre es inteligente y se preocupa por los demás supongo que va a encontrar una manera de salvar a todos. A medida que siga leyendo, averiguaré si estaba en lo cierto.

Destrezas de la semana

Comprensión: hacer y confirmar predicciones

Vocabulario: claves de contexto

Ortografía/Fonética: sílabas

Nombre _____

Tirar la moneda

Vamos a tirar una moneda diez veces. Pero antes de comenzar, vamos a predecir cuántas veces va a salir *heads* y cuántas veces va a salir *tails*. Podemos escribir abajo nuestra predicción. Cada vez que cae la moneda, vamos a hacer una marca en la tabla de conteo de la derecha. En matemáticas, este ejercicio se llama un problema de probabilidades.

Our Prediction

We think the coin will land heads _____ times.

We think the coin will land tails _____ times.

	HEADS	TAILS
1st toss		
2nd toss		
3rd toss		
4th toss		
5th toss		
6th toss		
7th toss		
8th toss		
9th toss		
10th toss		

The Results

The coin landed heads _____ times.

The coin landed tails _____ times.

Was our prediction correct? _____

Comprehension Check

Summarize

Use a Prediction Chart. List any predictions you made about who helps protect people during a hurricane. Tell whether your predictions were confirmed or not. Then summarize what you learned about hurricane heroes.

What I Predict	What Happens

Think and Compare

1. Look back at pages 10–12. Who would you have predicted to be on a FEMA rescue team? Were you surprised by any of the members? Why or why not? *(Make and Confirm Predictions)*

2. If you could be any kind of hurricane hero, which would you choose? Tell why. *(Synthesize)*

3. How is a hurricane similar to and different from another kind of storm that you know about? *(Apply)*

Hurricane HEROES

by Marc Gave

Table of Contents

Introduction

Winds scream. Rain pelts down. Buildings shudder. Trees sway back and forth. Branches break and fall to the ground. It's a hurricane!

You've probably seen pictures or images of hurricanes in a newspaper or on TV. What makes a storm a hurricane?

Glossary

data *(DAT-uh or DAY-tuh)* information, especially facts *(page 4)*

disaster *(di-ZAS-tuhr)* an event that causes much suffering or loss, such as a hurricane or a fire *(page 8)*

eye of the storm *(IGH UV THUH STAWRM)* the center of a hurricane that has no clouds and light winds *(page 4)*

specialist *(SPESH-uh-list)* a person who knows a great deal about something *(page 10)*

storm surge *(STAWRM SURJ)* a large dome of water that hits the coastline during a hurricane *(page 8)*

technology *(tek-NOL-uh-jee)* methods or machines that help people do jobs better and more quickly *(page 4)*

Index

Conclusion

There are all kinds of hurricane heroes. Some of them help people prepare for the storm. Others help during and after the storm.

Think about this: How would people get along in a hurricane without these heroes?

A happy rescue worker ➲ with his dog.

➲ Many telephone wires need repair after a hurricane.

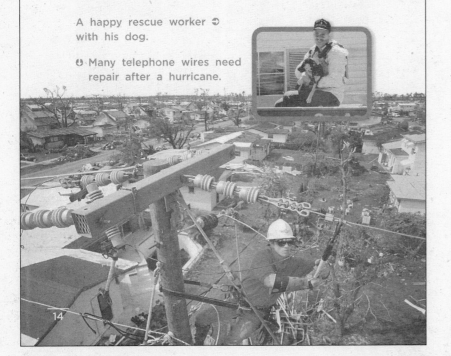

A hurricane is a storm with very strong winds and heavy rain. It starts over warm waters in an ocean. The storm might take the shape of a circle or an oval. It can be up to 400 miles (640 km) wide.

How do people prepare for hurricanes? How do "hurricane heroes" do their work? They do their jobs in offices and shelters. They are important before, during, and after a big storm. They help save lives.

↻ A hurricane's force is fierce.

Chapter 1
Predicting

How do people find out if a bad storm is coming?

Air Force pilots called hurricane hunters fly into the **eye of the storm**. They use the latest **technology** to get information about the storm. They follow the storm's path. Then they send all this **data** to the National Hurricane Center in Miami, Florida.

☝ Scientists also use photos of hurricanes taken from weather satellites circling Earth.

4

All kinds of workers help the people get what they need to go on with their lives. Some come to help clean up the mess. Others fix phone lines. Workers patch up roads. They rebuild walls to prevent floods. They test the water supply to make sure it is safe.

☝ In 2004, Hurricanes Charley, Frances, Ivan, and Jeanne all hit Florida.

Charley
Frances
Ivan
Jeanne

⋒ Firefighters in Miami, Florida clear a roadway
after hurricane Andrew downed trees.

FEMA workers spring into action again.
They sit down with families and listen
to their stories. Listening helps them
know how they can
help. The government
will loan money to
families so they
can fix up their
homes.

Fast Fact

Hurricane Katrina
in August of 2005
caused about $125
billion in damages.
It was the most
expensive hurricane
in United States
history.

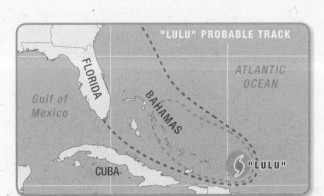

⋒ The dotted lines show areas where hurricanes
are most likely to travel.

Scientists at the center use the data
the pilots have gathered. They also use
data they have kept from past storms.
They know that almost all hurricanes start
between June and November. They know
that the worst month is
September. They have
maps that show where
storms have traveled.
From those, they
predict where a new
storm will move.

Fast Fact

A hurricane
has winds of at
least 74 miles
(120 km)
an hour.

National Hurricane Center

The National Hurricane Center keeps a constant watch on all storms. It issues warnings to the public.

The National Weather Service sends out reports 24 hours a day. People hear the reports over a special radio signal. The radio sounds an alarm if a bad storm is coming.

Police, state troopers, and people who set up shelters also help people escape from danger.

Fast Fact

The 24 to 36 hours before a storm hits is called a hurricane watch.

Chapter 4
Repairing

After a storm, many people return home numb with shock. Their houses may be gone. What is left may be a mess and in need of a lot of repair. Wind and rain may have ruined clothes and furniture. Businesses may have lost their goods. It can cost millions of dollars to replace these things. Who helps people get their lives back together again?

↺ This woman surveys what is left of a bedroom after Hurricane Jeanne hit on September 26, 2004.

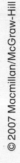

A rescue worker sends a dog to search for survivors after Hurricane Ivan destroyed this building.

During a storm, a tree may fall and hurt someone. Objects that are blowing around can hit a person too. People may be trapped in fallen buildings. FEMA workers from around the country are called on to help. They come to the rescue as soon as they can.

A FEMA task force has 62 well-trained **specialists**. Some are doctors who are there to help anyone who is injured during the storm. Some are engineers who can tell if a building has weakened and might fall. Some are searchers who may use boats or even helicopters to find missing people.

10

Chapter 2

Preparing

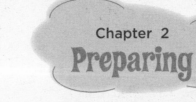

FEMA is a U.S. government agency. During a hurricane watch FEMA workers help people get ready for the storm. They explain what to do before the storm hits. They tell people if they need to leave their homes and go to a shelter. This safe place is usually on higher ground or in a building that can stand up to the storm.

Fast Fact

The letters in the name FEMA stand for Federal Emergency Management Agency.

Before people go to a shelter, they try to secure their homes.

7

The American Red Cross is another important group during a hurricane emergency. Red Cross workers set up shelters for people who have fled their homes due to a **disaster**. Red Cross workers also hand out food and blankets and provide medical care.

↻ The Red Cross hands out food and supplies to victims of a hurricane.

Fast Fact

A **storm surge** is a large swell of water, often 50 to 100 miles (80–160 km) wide.

© 2007 Macmillan/McGraw-Hill

Chapter 3
Rescuing

Some rescue workers help patrol the streets during a hurricane. If there is a lot of flooding, they travel in boats. They help people who get caught in their cars in the middle of a flooded street. They help others who are stranded in houses flooded with water.

↻ Hurricane heroes at work.

Fast Fact

Hurricanes have different names in different parts of the world. They are called cyclones when they happen over the Indian Ocean and typhoons in the western Pacific.

Word Workout

WORDS TO KNOW

architects   contain   hives   retreats

shallow   shelter   structures

Making a Statement I'll make a statement for each word. For the word *dams*, I might state: "Beavers live in these." You can give me the word above that matches each statement I make.

SPELLING WORDS

pilot   diner   tiger   favor   lemon

planet   model   shady   robot   tiny

label   cozy   silent   spider   frozen

Speed Spell I'll keep giving you words to spell, and at the end of one minute, we can see how many you spelled correctly. Do you want to go again to see if you can better your score?

(fold here)

Home-School Connection

Dear Family Member:

We're reading "Animal Homes" in class. The author is very good at describing animal homes. When she talks about honeybees, she says that the hive is made of waxy, six-sided cubicles. I can picture that in my mind. I know that the author is going to talk about a tower as tall as a giraffe, made by tiny termites. I can't wait to read about that!

This Week's Skills

Comprehension: description

Vocabulary: analogies

Spelling/Phonics: syllables

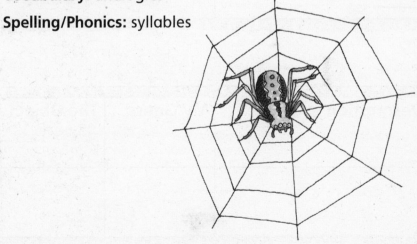

Name _____

Guess What I See

Think of an object in our home and give me one sentence that describes something about it. Don't name the object! I'll try to guess what it is, and if I can't, you can give me one more describing sentence, and then one more. We can use the chart to keep track of clues and guesses. Then I'll describe something for you to guess. We can play again on the opposite page.

Description	My Guess	The Object

Description	My Guess	The Object

Description	My Guess	The Object

Description	My Guess	The Object

Ejercicio de palabras

PALABRAS DE VOCABULARIO

architects	contain	hives	retreats
shallow	shelter	structures	

Decir una afirmación Voy a decir una oración afirmativa para cada palabra. Para la palabra *dams* podría decir: *Beavers live in these*. Tú dirás una palabra de arriba que se relacione con cada oración que digo.

PALABRAS DE ORTOGRAFÍA

pilot	diner	tiger	favor	lemon
planet	model	shady	robot	tiny
label	cozy	silent	spider	frozen

Ortografía veloz Te voy a dar varias palabras para deletrear y al cabo de un minuto podemos ver cuántas palabras deletreaste correctamente. ¿Quieres jugar de nuevo para ver si puedes mejorar tu puntaje?

(fold here)

Conexión con el hogar

Queridos familiares:

Estamos leyendo *Animal Homes* en la clase. La autora es muy buena para describir los hogares de los animales. Cuando habla de las abejas melíferas, ella dice que el panal está formado por cubículos hexagonales de cera. Yo puedo imaginarme eso. Sé que la autora va a hablar acerca de una torre tan alta como una jirafa construida por termitas diminutas. ¡Ya quiero leer acerca de eso!

Destrezas de la semana

Comprensión: descripciones

Vocabulario: analogías

Ortografía/Fonética: sílabas

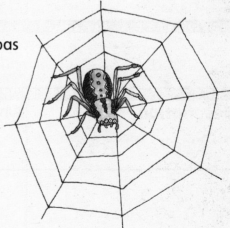

Nombre _____

Adivina lo que veo

Piensa en un objeto de nuestra casa y dame una descripción del mismo. ¡No menciones el nombre del objeto! Yo voy a intentar adivinar lo que es y si no puedo, me puedes dar otra descripción y después una descripción más. Podemos usar la tabla para anotar las pistas y las suposiciones. Luego, yo te daré una descripción. Podemos jugar de nuevo en la página siguiente.

Description	My Guess	The Object

Description	My Guess	The Object

Description	My Guess	The Object

Description	My Guess	The Object

Comprehension Check

Summarize

Complete a Description Web for this book. Then summarize the information you learned about birds.

Topic

Example

Detail Detail

Think and Compare

1. Reread page 4. What details did the author use to describe the tailorbird? *(Analyze Text Structure: Description)*

2. Which nests or bowers mentioned in this book do you find the most fascinating? Why? *(Synthesize)*

3. Many birds build their nests in trees. Yet people are cutting down many forests to build new homes and stores. What do you think might happen to bird populations as a result of this? Why do you think this may happen? *(Evaluate)*

16

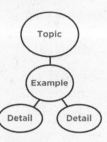

Amazing Bird Builders

by Carol Pugliano-Martin

Table of Contents

Introduction

They don't wear hard hats. They don't use machines. But most animals are amazing builders. Many different kinds of animals build their own homes. Their homes are structures that shelter them from the cold and the rain. They are also places where they can retreat from danger. Beavers build **lodges**, bees build hives, and birds build incredible nests where they hatch their eggs and raise their babies.

↻ A golden oriole feeds her chicks.

© 2007 Macmillan/McGraw-Hill

Glossary

architect (AHR-ki-tekt) a person who designs buildings and supervises their construction *(page 3)*

charcoal (CHAR-kohl) a soft, black form of carbon, made by partially burning wood *(page 10)*

colony (KOL-uh-nee) a group of animals or plants of the same kind that live together *(page 5)*

fiber (FIGH-buhr) a long, thin thread of material *(page 4)*

lodge (LOJ) a beaver's home *(page 2)*

mate (MAYT) the male or female of a pair of animals *(page 5)*

species (SPEE-sheez) a group of animals or plants that have many characteristics in common. Members of the same species can mate and have offspring. *(page 14)*

Index

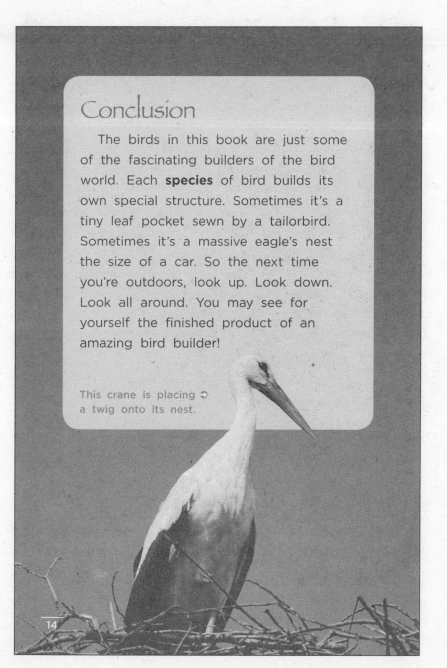

Conclusion

The birds in this book are just some of the fascinating builders of the bird world. Each **species** of bird builds its own special structure. Sometimes it's a tiny leaf pocket sewn by a tailorbird. Sometimes it's a massive eagle's nest the size of a car. So the next time you're outdoors, look up. Look down. Look all around. You may see for yourself the finished product of an amazing bird builder!

This crane is placing ⟳ a twig onto its nest.

Have you ever seen a bird's nest? Some are made of twigs and are round and shallow. Others are made of grass and are long and deep. Still others are made from mud and look like small cups. There are even birds that use their own saliva, or spit, when they build a nest. Many birds' nests contain feathers and hair. This makes the nest a soft place for their babies, or chicks, to sleep. Birds are some of the most amazing **architects** in the animal world!

This altimira oriole ⌒ seems comfortable in its large nest.

⟲ Robins lay three eggs in their nests.

CHAPTER 1
Tailors and Weavers

Have you ever seen a bird sew? You would if you watched a tailorbird. It can stitch its nest together the way a tailor sews clothes. Tailorbirds use their beaks as needles. They use vegetable **fiber** as thread to sew the edges of leaves together. This makes a little pocket. The bird lays its eggs in this pocket and raises its chicks there. Tailorbirds even tie knots in the thread to keep the pocket from falling apart!

↻ Tailorbirds are found in Malaysia and the Philippines, as well as China and India.

♬ A tailorbird

Plastic Rings

Milk companies in Australia stopped making the plastic rings on milk bottles blue. These rings attracted male satin bowerbirds. But they were dangerous because they could get stuck around the bird's neck.

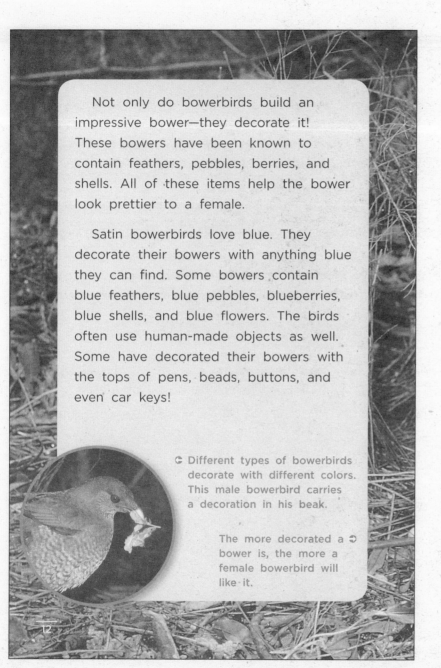

Not only do bowerbirds build an impressive bower—they decorate it! These bowers have been known to contain feathers, pebbles, berries, and shells. All of these items help the bower look prettier to a female.

Satin bowerbirds love blue. They decorate their bowers with anything blue they can find. Some bowers contain blue feathers, blue pebbles, blueberries, blue shells, and blue flowers. The birds often use human-made objects as well. Some have decorated their bowers with the tops of pens, beads, buttons, and even car keys!

↻ Different types of bowerbirds decorate with different colors. This male bowerbird carries a decoration in his beak.

The more decorated a ↻ bower is, the more a female bowerbird will like it.

12

A male weaverbird hangs from his nest and makes noise to attract a female.

One of the best architects of the bird world is the weaverbird. This bird weaves hundreds of pieces of grass together to make its home. Male weaverbirds build nests to attract **mates**. The best nests attract the most attention.

Other types of weaverbirds build giant **colonies** of nests. The colonies are like bird apartment houses. In fact, they can house up to 500 birds!

Most weaverbirds live ↻ in South Africa.

5

© 2007 Macmillan/McGraw-Hill

CHAPTER 2

Eagle Nests

Eagles build the largest nests in the bird world. Some can be almost 10 feet (3 m) long! Bald eagles build their nests in the tops of trees that are near water. They eat fish so they build nests that are close to their food.

Bald Eagle

Summer range

Winter range

Year-round range

Eagles live over most of North America, from Alaska and Canada to northern Mexico.

Eagles choose high spots for their nests so they can see everything going on around them.

6

11

CHAPTER 3
The Bowerbird

Now you know that birds build amazing nests. But birds build other things as well. Male bowerbirds build shelters called bowers to attract females. The bowers are built on the ground. They are little huts made of twigs, leaves, and moss. Males with the best bowers get the attention of the females.

After people build a house, they finish the job by painting it. There is one kind of bowerbird that paints his bower too! The satin bowerbird paints the walls of his bower with chewed berries or **charcoal**.

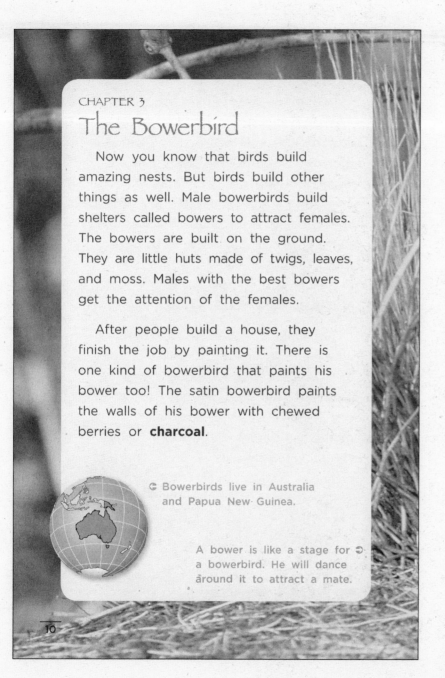

↺ Bowerbirds live in Australia and Papua New Guinea.

A bower is like a stage for ↺ a bowerbird. He will dance around it to attract a mate.

The eagle's nest is made mostly of sticks of many sizes. The eagles place these sticks in layers. The first layer is made in the shape of a triangle. The next layer is an upside-down triangle. They keep building like this until the nest is finished. Then they line their nest with moss, pine needles, or grass. This helps keep the chicks warm and comfortable when they hatch.

| Step 1 | Step 2 | Step 3 |

Big Sticks
Big nests need big sticks! The sticks eagles use to build their nests can be up to 8 feet long!

Most birds build a new nest each year. But eagles can use the same nest for up to fifteen years. Each year they add sticks to the nest to make it larger and larger. A nest may start out measuring about 3 feet (1 m) across and 1 foot (0.3 m) deep. Then, as the years go by, it can become as large as 10 feet (3 m) across and 15 feet (4.5 m) deep! A human being could rest quite comfortably in an eagle's nest.

The world's biggest eagle's nest was found in Florida. It was 9 1/2 feet (3 m) across and 20 feet (6 m) high! This nest was probably used for about one hundred years. It weighed more than 2 tons, or 4,000 pounds (1,800 kg)! That's as heavy as a large car!

Eagles lay one to three ➲ cream-colored eggs in their big nests.

Word Workout

WORDS TO KNOW

appliances	construction	downtown
equipment	leaky	owners

Word Meanings Let's look at these words. Pronounce each one and tell me what it means. Then we can use one of the words to make a sentence about our home.

SPELLING WORDS

riddle	nickel	towel	tunnel	squirrel
travel	puzzle	camel	purple	able
pickle	little	handle	castle	eagle

Spell the L's The spelling words on this list end with the letters **el** or **le**. I'll say each word and you can tell me what the words end with. Then you can spell the complete word.

(fold here)

© Macmillan/McGraw-Hill

Home-School Connection

Dear Family Member:

We're reading *A Castle on Viola Street*. It's about a family who wants to live in a nice house. The family and the neighbors work together to fix up old houses so that people can live in them. We learned that the theme is the message of the story. I think the theme in this book is that helping one another can lead to wonderful things.

This Week's Skills

Comprehension: theme

Vocabulary: context clues

Spelling/Phonics: words with **el** and **le**

Name _____

Theme Parties

A theme party is about one idea. People might wear red, white, and blue clothes to a July 4th party. There might be American flags there. People might sing songs about our country. Let's plan our own theme parties. We can decide what we want at each one.

Team Celebration

Where?

Decorations?

Costumes?

Games?

Thanksgiving

Where?

Decorations?

Costumes?

Games?

New Year's Day

Where?

Decorations?

Costumes?

Games?

Ejercicio de palabras

PALABRAS DE VOCABULARIO

appliances	construction	downtown
equipment	leaky	owners

Significado de las palabras Observemos estas palabras. Pronuncia cada una y dime lo que significan. Luego, podemos usar una de las palabras para hacer una oración acerca de nuestra casa.

PALABRAS DE ORTOGRAFÍA

riddle	nickel	towel	tunnel	squirrel
travel	puzzle	camel	purple	able
pickle	little	handle	castle	eagle

Deletrea las letras L Las palabras de ortografía de esta lista termina con las letras **el** o **le**. Voy a decir cada palabra y tú me dirás con qué letras terminan las palabras. Luego, puedes deletrear la palabra completa.

(fold here)

© Macmillan/McGraw-Hill

Conexión con el hogar

Queridos familiares:

Estamos leyendo *A Castle on Viola Street*. El cuento es acerca de una familia que quiere vivir en una casa bonita. La familia y los vecinos trabajan juntos para arreglar casas viejas para que la gente viva en ellas. Aprendimos que el tema es el mensaje de un relato. Pienso que el tema de este libro es que ayudarse mutuamente puede llevar a cosas maravillosas.

Destrezas de la semana

Comprensión: tema

Vocabulario: claves de contexto

Ortografía/Fonética: palabras con **el** y **le**

Nombre _____

Fiestas temáticas

Una fiesta temática se organiza en torno a un tema. La gente podría vestir ropa roja, blanca y azul para una fiesta del 4 de julio. Podría haber banderas estadounidenses. La gente podría cantar canciones patrióticas. Planeemos nuestras propias fiestas temáticas. Podemos decidir lo que queremos que haya en cada una.

Team Celebration

Where?

Decorations?

Costumes?

Games?

Thanksgiving

Where?

Decorations?

Costumes?

Games?

Happy Birthday Cinco de Mayo

Where?

Decorations?

Costumes?

Games?

Comprehension Check

Summarize

Use a Theme Map to record clues and the theme, or main idea, of the story. Then use the chart to summarize the story.

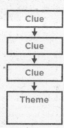

Think and Compare

1. Reread page 12. What is the main idea of this page? *(Analyze Theme)*

2. What steps can you take if you have an emergency in your home? To whom should you go for help? *(Apply)*

3. Many towns have volunteer firefighters. Volunteers do not get paid. Why is volunteer work important? *(Evaluate)*

© 2007 Macmillan/McGraw-Hill

EMERGENCY!

by Lisa Norby
illustrated by Paul Gibbs

Table of Contents

Chapter 1 Fluffy the Alligator

Susan and Emma's parents were packing the car for an overnight trip. "I'm sorry we can't take you kids along this time," their mother told them. "I'm sure you'll be fine with Aunt Claire. At least I think you will."

"Don't be silly," said their father. "Your sister is highly capable. What could go wrong?"

Before anyone could answer his question, Aunt Claire's car turned into the driveway. She scrambled out. "I hope I'm not late," she said. "I had some important business downtown, and I just lost track of the time."

"You could try wearing a watch," her sister said.

2

Afterwards, the firefighters gave Susan a tour. She saw the beds where the firefighters slept. She saw the dummy that they used to teach CPR. She slid down the firefighter's pole, and even got to sit in the driver's seat of the fire truck. She pictured herself becoming a volunteer firefighter some day. She'd be ready for any emergency, including a flood in a basement.

Emergency!

© 2007 Macmillan/McGraw-Hill

15

That was how Aunt Claire became a cook for the volunteer firefighters' pancake breakfast. Susan helped out in the kitchen too.

They made the best pancakes ever with apples, blueberries, and bananas. They had syrup, butter, jam and powdered sugar to top off the pancakes.

One of the firefighters came to the griddle and showed off by flipping some pancakes in the air and catching them on a plate. He bowed to his clapping audience.

© 2007 Macmillan/McGraw-Hill

Emergency!

Aunt Claire waved her arms. Silver bracelets jangled on both wrists. "Watches are so dull and practical," she said. "I prefer fun things."

Aunt Claire was the owner of a store called The Junque Shoppe. That was a fancy way of saying that she sold junk. Some of the things in the store were antiques, but others were just old.

Aunt Claire did give good presents, though.

This time she had a pretty box filled with old beads for Susan. For four-year-old Emma she had a stuffed alligator.

The minute Emma saw the alligator she forgot all about saying goodbye to her mom and dad. "Fluffy can sit on my bed," she announced.

"Fluffy isn't a good name for an alligator," Susan said.

"Don't upset your sister," her mom warned.

Susan rolled her eyes. She was just trying to be helpful.

Mom and dad finally said their goodbyes and left. After dinner, Emma sat down to watch a video about dinosaurs. Susan looked at her beads.

4

"Okay," said the men in unison.

Aunt Claire waved her hands. "I wish there was something I could do to make it up to you."

"We're having a pancake breakfast next Saturday to raise money for a new fire truck," he said. "We sure could use another griddle cook."

13

At that moment, Susan heard a siren outside the house. She went upstairs. Two firefighters were at the front door. "Is everyone here all right?" the taller one asked.

"It's over," Susan told them showing them into the house. "The basement was flooding. But I figured out how to turn the water off."

Aunt Claire looked embarrassed. "I'm sorry for bothering you guys. I guess I got too excited."

"We volunteer firefighters respond to all kinds of emergencies," the tall man said. "But next time you might try asking one of your neighbors for help first."

"Actually, we were curious," the other firefighter said. "We've never had an alligator emergency before."

"Fluffy," said Emma. "His name is Fluffy."

12

Emergency!

"Let's make some popcorn," said Aunt Claire.

Susan got out the popcorn box. Her aunt started cutting open one package and pouring it into a pan.

"No!" Susan yelped. "Not like that! You put the whole package in the microwave."

"How about that!" said Aunt Claire. "I don't have these fancy appliances in my kitchen. I guess I just don't understand them."

5

Chapter 2 The Flood

Aunt Claire might be impractical in some ways. But when it came to real food, she knew how to cook. The next morning, she made delicious blueberry pancakes for breakfast. She even showed Emma how to decorate them with smiley faces made of blueberries and bananas.

Susan had soccer practice that afternoon. When breakfast was over she decided to collect her things. Her socks were still in the dryer. But when she started down the steps to the basement she got a big surprise.

© 2007 Macmillan/McGraw-Hill

Emergency!

Susan wanted to figure out this water problem. The water level was rising. Suddenly, she had an idea. There was a closet next to the laundry room where her parents kept old toys and sports equipment. She looked inside and saw the water meter. Underneath it was a large valve. That was where her mom had shut off the water.

She turned the valve. The water spewing from the pipe slowed to a trickle. Then it stopped. Susan took a deep breath and relaxed.

Chapter 3 The Firefighters

Along the far wall of the basement were shelves stuffed with old books, tools, and boxes of winter clothes. "Those plumbers won't call back for hours," Aunt Claire said. "By then, everything will be ruined. I'm going to call the firehouse. Someone there will know what to do."

Aunt Claire ran back up the stairs. Susan stayed behind. She was sure there was another valve somewhere. She could hear her aunt up in the kitchen, talking on the phone. "I have an emergency here. There are two children in the house," she heard her aunt saying. "The whole place is filling up." Her aunt sounded frantic.

Emma was in the kitchen too. She was running around, shrieking, "Alligator! Alligator!"

10

Water poured from a leaky pipe in the corner. The floor was flooded. The water was two inches deep and rising fast.

She rushed back to the kitchen to warn her aunt. "I think we have a problem," Susan said.

7

At first, Aunt Claire was calm. She sat down at the kitchen table and started calling plumbers. But it was Sunday morning. No one was at work. Some of the plumbers had answering machines, and Aunt Claire left the same message for all of them. "Please call back. It's an emergency. We have a flood here."

Susan tried to figure out what her mother would do. "Maybe there's a way to turn the water off," she said. "I think mom did it once when the construction workers were adding the extra bathroom."

"I'll go check," Aunt Claire said. "But if you're going to come with me, put your rain boots on. There's no telling what's floating around down there."

© 2007 Macmillan/McGraw-Hill

Emergency!

Emma was listening in the doorway. Her eyes grew wide. "Are there alligators down there?" she asked. She looked hopeful.

"No," Susan told her. "Fluffy is the only alligator in this house." She pulled on her boots to make her aunt happy.

When she got to the basement, Aunt Claire was peering behind the washing machine. There was a maze of pipes. Each of them had a turn-off valve. Aunt Claire tried them all. But water continued to pour from the leaky pipe in the corner.

Word Workout

WORDS TO KNOW

boasting   conversation   interrupted   rebuild

scrambled   seized   sway

Community Clean-Up Let's use the words to talk about what our community can do to clean up.

SPELLING WORDS

resell   repay   return   reprint

disagree dislike   disappear unafraid

unwrap   unbeaten untied   precook

preheat   prepay   preschool

Switching I'll give you a word to spell. Then tell me which of the other prefixes you might be able to use at the beginning of the word. Some words will only work with one prefix.

Home-School Connection

Dear Family Member:

We're reading "Wilbur's Boast" this week. It's part of a book called *Charlotte's Web*. In it, Wilbur the pig tries to weave a web like the one Charlotte the spider spins. Wilbur tries but he fails. Then he tries again. I'm making a judgment that Wilbur is an animal who tries hard to do what he wants.

This Week's Skills

Comprehension: make judgments

Vocabulary: adding **re, un, dis,** and **pre**

Spelling/Phonics: words with **re, un, dis,** and **pre**

Name _____

Right or Wrong?

Let's each place a marker on Start. Toss a penny, and if it comes up "heads," move one space. If it comes up "tails," move two spaces. Make a judgment. Does the picture show something that helps the environment or hurts the environment? Score a point for something helpful. We'll take turns. At the end, we'll see who has the most points.

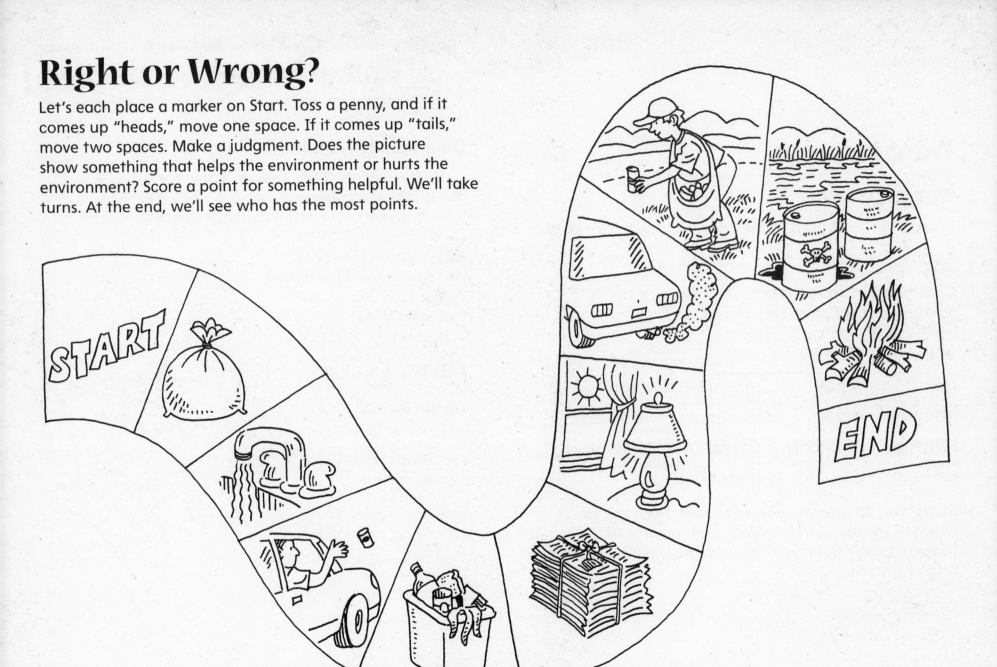

Ejercicio de palabras

PALABRAS DE VOCABULARIO

boasting   conversation   interrupted   rebuild

scrambled   seized   sway

Limpieza de la comunidad Usemos las palabras para hablar acerca de lo que nuestra comunidad puede hacer para realizar una limpieza.

PALABRAS DE ORTOGRAFÍA

resell   repay   return   reprint

disagree   dislike   disappear   unafraid

unwrap   unbeaten   untied   precook

preheat   prepay   preschool

Cambiar prefijos Te voy a dar una palabra para deletrear. Luego, dime cuál de los otros prefijos podrías usar al principio de la palabra. Algunas palabras funcionan sólo con un prefijo.

© Macmillan/McGraw-Hill

(fold here)

Conexión con el hogar

Queridos familiares:

Estamos leyendo *Wilbur's Boast* esta semana. Es parte de un libro que se llama *Charlotte's Web*. En el cuento, Wilbur, el cerdito, intenta tejer una red como la que teje Charlotte, la araña. Wilbur lo intenta pero fracasa. Entonces lo intenta de nuevo. Yo opino que Wilbur es un animal que se esfuerza mucho en hacer lo que quiere.

Destrezas de la semana

Comprensión: hacer jucios

Vocabulario: añadir **re, un, dis** y **pre**

Ortografía/Fonética: palabras con **re, un, dis** y **pre**

Nombre _____

¿Bueno o malo?

Coloquemos una ficha cada uno en donde dice *START*.
Tira una moneda de un centavo. Si sale *heads*, mueve un
espacio. Si sale *tails*, mueve dos espacios. Da una opinión. ¿La
ilustración muestra algo que beneficia al medio ambiente
o lo daña? Anota un tanto para algo que sea beneficioso.
Vamos a tomar turnos. Al final, veremos quién tiene la mayor
cantidad de puntos.

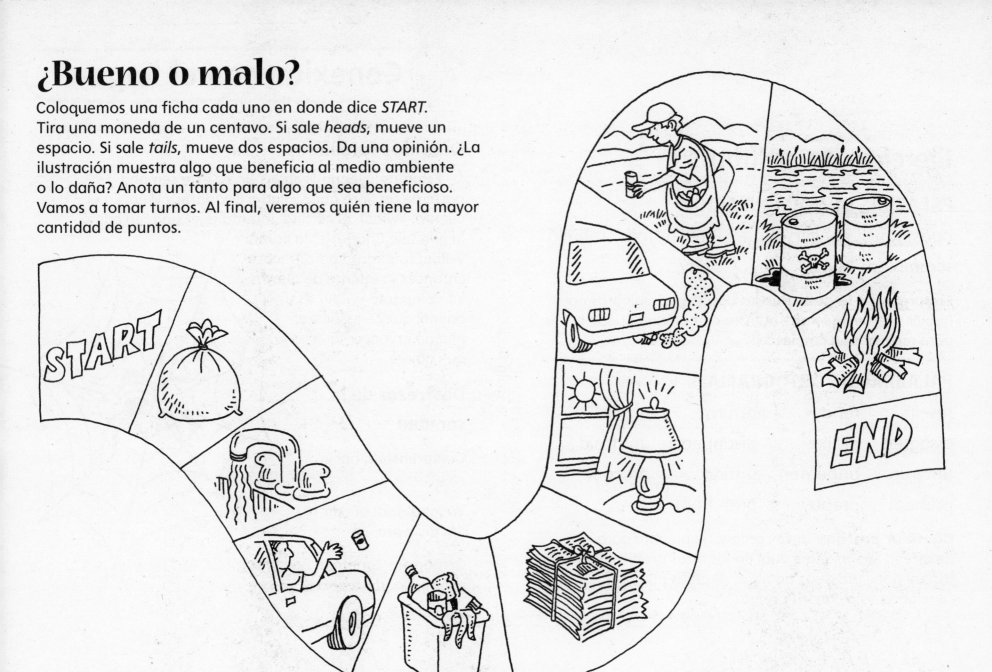

Comprehension Check

Summarize

Use a Judgment Chart to record actions and make judgments about the story. Then answer this question: How did Ellen and Artie's joke help Mike find a new friend?

Action	→	Judgment
	→	

Think and Compare

1. Read the conversation between Mike and Artie on page 5. How does Mike feel about Ellen? *(Make Judgments)*

2. How would you feel if you were misjudged by someone who didn't know you? How would you change the person's mind? *(Apply)*

3. Why is it important not to judge people before you really know them? *(Evaluate)*

16

Mike's Surprise

by Susan Blackaby

illustrated by Bernadette Lau

Table of Contents

Chapter 1
Artie's Lesson

Mike Drake worked as the night custodian at Riverside School. Each night, he went from classroom to classroom, mopping and cleaning. Mike liked to take his late-night snack break when he got to Room 4. While he ate his snack, he taught Artie, the Room 4 parakeet, to talk. He gave Artie a lesson almost every night.

"Yoo-hoo, Artie." Mike seized the cover of the parakeet's cage and pulled it off. "It is your good buddy, Mike. How is my pretty bird?"

"Take it easy, Bright Eyes," he said.

"I will," said Ellen, rearranging her nest.

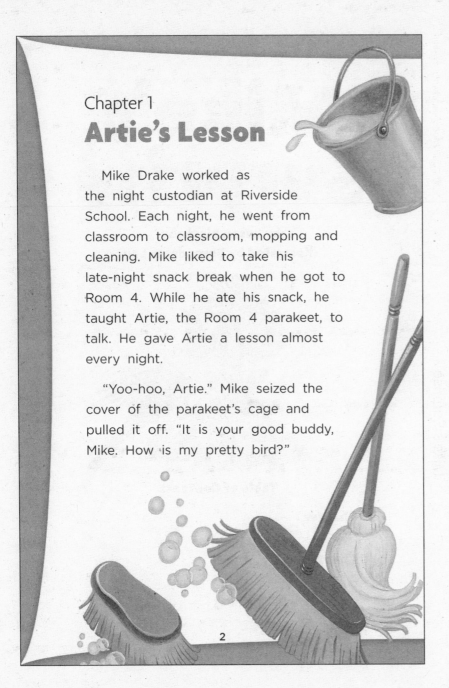

"*Nocturnal* means active at night. *Diurnal* means active during the day," said Ellen.

"Oh, I see," said Artie. "So you and Mike are both nocturnal."

Mike and Ellen laughed.

"I guess you could say that," said Mike.

Ellen and Artie shared Mike's lunch and kept him company while he worked.

Ellen discussed information posted on the Current Events bulletin board. Artie flew from the teacher's desk to the light fixture. When it was time to go, Mike set them in their cages for the night.

"Sleep tight, pretty bird," said Mike. He covered Artie's cage.

"Okay," said Artie.

Mike picked up his bucket and mop.

14

Mike always interrupted Artie's sleep. Artie was never prepared for this nightly wake-up call. He blinked and looked around.

"Artie, are you ready for your vocabulary lesson?" asked Mike.

"Okay," said Artie. He hopped onto his swing and began to sway.

"Who is that pretty bird?" said Mike. "What is that pretty bird's name?"

3

"R—T," said Artie. The swing squeaked as it went back and forth.

Mike clapped. He loved getting Artie to talk.

Mike opened up the cage door so that Artie could hop out onto his finger.

"Hey, Artie, who is your fuzzy pal here?" Mike pointed at the cage on the table. Peeking out from the shavings was Ellen, the Room 4 hamster.

"L—N," said Artie.

"Good for you!" said Mike.

"How do you do," she said. "I am very pleased to meet you. I hope you can recover your wits. It was unkind of us to scare you like that. We just wanted to have a little fun."

Mike's voice came unstuck. "It was just kind of a shock," he said.

"You are probably wondering why we did not speak up before now," said Artie. "The truth is that until you started giving me lessons, I could not talk very well. And I had no idea that Ellen could talk at all. Until you came along, we were never awake at the same time to have a chat."

"That is right," said Ellen. "After all, I am nocturnal. Artie is diurnal."

Artie cocked his head. "I recall hearing those words in science class, but I don't remember what they mean."

"See, what did I tell you," said Artie. "Isn't she amazing?"

Mike nodded. He looked as white as a sheet, and he was still unable to speak.

"Are you okay, Mike? Maybe you should sit down before you keel over," said Artie.

Mike sat down. His hand shook as he unlatched the door to Ellen's cage. She trotted out onto the table.

© 2007 Macmillan/McGraw-Hill

Mike's Surprise

Ellen scrambled up on top of her cardboard shelter to listen. Her back legs wiggled as she pulled herself up onto the roof.

"What kind of eyes does Ellen have?" asked Mike.

"*B—D*," said Artie.

"She has beady little eyes! You are so right! What kind of brain does Ellen have?" asked Mike.

"*M—T*," said Artie.

"Yes sir, her brain is as empty as a pocket," said Mike.

Ellen hopped down into her shavings and started digging.

"Look. Ellen just rebuilds her nest over and over. That is all she does!" Mike put Artie on his shoulder. "Now here's a hard one, Artie. Pay attention. What is another word for *boring*?"

"*T—D—S*," said Artie.

"Tedious! You got it!" said Mike.

Ellen gave a little snort.

"Tedious is the word for it, all right," she thought. "I am bored stiff." Ellen squeaked and wriggled down into her nest.

6

© 2007 Macmillan/McGraw-Hill

Mike was shaking his head as if he were trying to wake himself up from a dream.

"Really, Mike, you have to check this out. Ellen, what is 3 x 3?" asked Artie.

"Nine," said Ellen.

"What is 2 x 8?" asked Artie.

"Sixteen," said Ellen. She smiled at Mike. Her sharp little teeth were gleaming. Her bright eyes glittered. Mike gaped at her.

"What is 7 x 5?" asked Artie.

"Thirty-five," said Ellen.

11

The next night, Mike and Artie were having their usual conversation.

"What kind of brain does Ellen have?" asked Mike.

"I know you want me to say *M—T*, Mike, but actually Ellen is really smart," said Artie. He hopped up and down Mike's finger.

"What did you say?" Mike asked.

"Ellen knows all sorts of stuff. She can recite the 50 states in alphabetical order. She can make a bar graph. She can write a book report. She even knows math."

10

"Try this one, Artie," said Mike. "What is another word for *sneaky*?"

"*D—V—S*," said Artie.

"Devious!" said Mike. "Artie, my fine feathered friend, you are unbelievable." Mike gave Artie some of his apple and then carried him around on his shoulder while he mopped the floor.

Finally Mike returned Artie to his cage.

"See you tomorrow, Artie," said Mike.

"OK," said Artie.

Mike pulled the cover down over Artie's cage. Then he picked up his mop and his bucket and left the room.

7

Chapter 2
Ellen's Plan

The second Mike was gone, Ellen hopped back up onto her box. Artie peeked out at her through a slit in his cover.

"Empty? You think my head is empty?" Ellen stomped her back foot. "I beg your pardon, Artie, but between you and me, who is smarter?" she asked.

"*U—R*," said Artie.

Ellen paced on top of her box. She sputtered and huffed.

"I do not mean to sound like I am boasting, but who knows how to prepare popcorn in the microwave? Who knows how to undo a lunchbox latch? Who knows multiplication up to tensies?"

© 2007 Macmillan/McGraw-Hill

"*U*," said Artie. "*U, u, u.*" Artie chuckled. Then he said, "Mike isn't such a bad guy, Ellen. He just doesn't like your sharp little teeth. He is afraid you might bite."

"I do not intend to bite him," said Ellen, "but I might give him a piece of my empty mind. I could show him a thing or two."

Ellen giggled. "Hey, Artie, here is an idea. Tomorrow night when Mike comes, interrupt your lesson with a little chitchat."

"Ellen, you are so devious," said Artie. "Mike will be speechless."

Word Workout

WORDS TO KNOW

automatically dispute historical requirements

Back in Time Think about someplace you would like to be a long, long time ago. Let's talk about how you could get there using each of the words.

SPELLING WORDS

sister	winter	December	doctor	trailer
writer	sailor	dollar	later	silver
author	mayor	cellar	toaster	dancer

Speed Spell I'm going to look at the clock and ask you to spell each of these words out loud. At the end of the minute, I'll tell you how many you got right. We can go over those you missed. Want to try again?

(fold here)

Home-School Connection

Dear Family Member:

In class we are reading the article "An American Hero Flies Again." It's about astronaut John Glenn and the space program. I'm learning to look for the problem in an article and the steps that lead to solving it. When America wanted to land a man on the moon, it was John Glenn who worked on the inside layout and the controls. His work led to Neil Armstrong's moon landing. Those were big problems and complicated solutions. But small problems can be solved the same way, one step at a time.

This Week's Skills

Comprehension: problem and solution

Vocabulary: Greek roots

Spelling/Phonics: words ending with **er, ar,** or **or**

Name _____

Helping Harry

Let's think about Harry's problem and decide upon three steps Harry could take to reach a solution.

Harry's Problem: He wants the new video game at the mall, but he doesn't have money for it.

"I've got an idea," he said.

So he:

Then he:

And at last:

Saving Suzy

Now let's help Suzy solve her problem.

Suzy's Problem: She wants pizza for dinner but her mother wants to make soup.

"I've got an idea," she said.

So she:

Then she:

And at last:

Ejercicio de palabras

PALABRAS DE VOCABULARIO

automatically   dispute   historical   requirements

Retroceder en el tiempo Piensa en un lugar de hace mucho tiempo atrás en el que te gustaría estar. Hablemos acerca de cómo podrías llegar allí usando cada una de las palabras.

PALABRAS DE ORTOGRAFÍA

sister	winter	December	doctor	trailer
writer	sailor	dollar	later	silver
author	mayor	cellar	toaster	dancer

Ortografía veloz Voy a mirar el reloj y te voy a pedir que deletrees cada una de estas palabras en voz alta. Al cabo de un minuto, te diré cuántas palabras deletreaste correctamente. Podemos revisar las que no pudiste deletrear correctamente. ¿Quieres intentarlo de nuevo?

·········(fold here)·········

Queridos familiares:

En la clase estamos leyendo el artículo *An American Hero Flies Again*. Es acerca del astronauta John Glenn y el programa espacial. Estoy aprendiendo a buscar el problema en un artículo y los pasos que llevan a resolverlo. Cuando Estados Unidos llévo al hombre a la Luna, John Glenn trabajó en la disposición del interior de la nave y los controles. Su trabajo llevó a que Neil Armstrong pisara la Luna. Esos eran problemas grandes y soluciones complicadas. Pero los pequeños problemas pueden ser resueltos de la misma manera, un paso por vez.

Destrezas de la semana

Compresión: problema y solución

Vocabulario: raices del griego

Ortografía/Fonética: palabras que termine con **er, ar** o **or**

Nombre _____

Ayudar a Harry

Pensemos acerca del problema de Harry y decidamos tres pasos que Harry debería tomar para alcanzar una solución.

Harry's Problem: He wants the new video game at the mall, but he doesn't have money for it.

"I've got an idea," he said.

So he:

Then he:

And at last:

Salvar a Suzy

Ahora ayudemos a Suzy a resolver su problema.

Suzy's Problem: She wants pizza for dinner but her mother wants to make soup out of tulips.

"I've got an idea," she said.

So she:

Then she:

And at last:

Comprehension Check

Summarize

Use the pictures and captions to organize the information in this book. Then tell about the problems some people had to overcome to vote, and summarize what you learned about voting.

Think and Compare

1. Reread page 6. What problems did African Americans face when they tried to vote? *(Identify Problem and Solution)*

2. Think of a time when you voted for something in school or at home. What was it for? Tell about it. *(Synthesize)*

3. Why do you think people are willing to fight for rights, like the right to vote? *(Evaluate)*

16

Getting Out the Vote

by Steven Otfinoski

Table of Contents

Introduction

We have many rights as **citizens**. One of these is the right to vote. When we cast our vote, we elect the people we want to **represent** us in government.

We vote for many public leaders. Some run our town, like the mayor. Some are in state government. Others work for us in Washington, D.C. These include our lawmakers. We also vote for President and Vice President.

Some people show IDs before they vote.

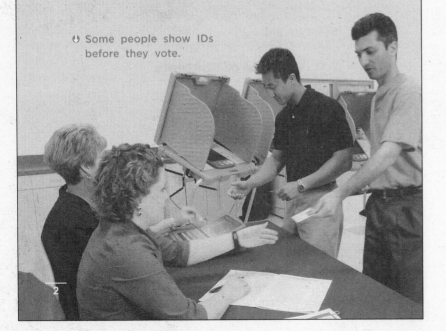

2

Glossary

abridge *(uh-BRIJ)* to reduce in scope *(page 5)*

amendment *(uh-MEND-muhnt)* a formal change *(page 5)*

citizen *(SIT-uh-zuhn)* a person who was born in a country or who chooses to live in and become a member of a country *(page 2)*

Congress *(KONG-gris)* a branch of the government of the United States that makes laws *(page 9)*

register *(REJ-uh-stuhr)* to place your name on a list or record *(page 11)*

represent *(rep-ri-ZENT)* to speak or act for *(page 2)*

resident *(REZ-i-dunt)* a person who lives in a particular place *(page 3)*

Index

15

Conclusion

Voting is an important right. Voting gives people a say in how the government is run and who runs it. It gives them the power to say who represents them in the government. It is a way to make sure that everyone's voice is heard.

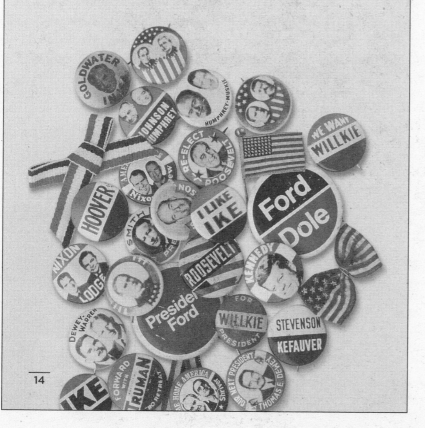

Who can vote? There are some requirements. Voters must be 18 years old. They must be citizens of the United States, and they must be **residents** of the town or city where they vote. Voters do not have to be rich, and they can be of any religion.

But it wasn't always this way. Certain groups of people had to fight for the right to vote.

⟳ These people are voting on electronic machines.

Chapter One

From the Few to the Many

During the time of the American colonies very few people could vote. You had to be a rich white man who owned land.

Back then leaders felt that voting was too important to be left to just anyone. These men elected others who were very much like themselves.

This system continued on even after the United States became a free nation.

↻ This painting shows George Washington and others who signed the United States Constitution.

4

Fast Facts

- People vote for President of the United States every four years.
- One day we might even vote for President on the Internet.

In some states you vote by checking off your choice on a paper ballot. In other states you vote by punching a card. You might also vote on a voting machine.

The newest way to vote is by computer. You press a box on a computer screen next to your choice's name.

This woman used a ↻ paper ballot to cast her vote.

BALLOTS

13

You vote at a **polling place** near where you live. It's usually in a school, town hall, or other building. Every voter is given a specific place to vote.

At the polling place, you check in at a table. Workers check off your name on the voting lists. You may have to sign in too. This way they make sure that each person only votes once.

Now you head to the voting booth. It's time to cast your vote.

Absentee Voting

What happens if you're out of your voting district when there's an election? You can still vote—by absentee ballot. If you know you're going to be away, you can vote before you leave. Or you can mail in your ballot. Many people vote by absentee ballot. Disabled, sick, and elderly people are allowed to vote early too.

© 2007 Macmillan/McGraw-Hill

In the 1820s some states began changing the rules. Voters did not have to own property anymore—but they still had to be white males.

By the 1840s all white men were automatically allowed to vote. But women couldn't vote. Neither could African American people.

In 1863 slavery ended. In 1870 the Fifteenth **Amendment** to the Constitution gave African Americans the right to vote. This was an important historical event. But not all Southern states wanted to share power with African Americans. So they set up ways to keep them from voting.

IT'S THE LAW

"The right of citizens of the United States to vote shall not be denied or **abridged** by the United States or by any state on account of race, color, or previous condition of servitude."

—Fifteenth Amendment

Some Southern states passed a poll tax. People had to pay it before they could vote. Many African Americans didn't have the money to pay a poll tax.

Some states also made voters take tests. Many African Americans hadn't been taught to read and write, so they couldn't pass the tests.

Those who could read and write were given hard tests about state laws. This unjust system was in place for a long time in some parts of the South even after the Supreme Court ruled against it in 1915.

Voting Rights for Everyone

- The Twenty-fourth Amendment to the Constitution states that poll taxes are against the law.

- In 1965 Congress passed the Voting Rights Act. All citizens, no matter what the color of their skin, could vote.

© 2007 Macmillan/McGraw-Hill

Chapter Two

How We Vote

How do you vote? First, you must sign up or **register** to vote in your town or city when you turn 18.

When can you register? In some states you must sign up 30 days before an election in order to vote. In other states you can register up until the day of the election.

Election day is the first Tuesday after the first Monday in November. It is a legal holiday in most states.

IT'S THE LAW

"The right of citizens of the United States to vote shall not be denied or abridged by the United States or by any State on account of sex. Congress shall have the power to enforce this article by appropriate legislation."
—Nineteenth Amendment

IT'S THE LAW

"The right of citizens of the United States, who are eighteen years of age or older, to vote shall not be denied or abridged by the United States or by any state on account of age."
—Twenty-sixth Amendment

Until 1971 people had to be 21 years of age to vote. Now 18-year-olds can vote. How did this change come about? Many soldiers who fought and died in the Vietnam War were as young as 18. Most people did not dispute the idea that if 18-year-olds were old enough to fight for their country, then they were old enough to vote.

↻ Young men and women serve in the armed forces.

10

In the 1960s, things finally began to change. Reverend Martin Luther King, Jr., and others led protests and marches to demand rights, such as the right to vote. Congress passed laws that outlawed the poll tax and protected voting rights.

↻ Martin Luther King, Jr., waves to the crowd at a civil rights march in Washington, DC., on August 28, 1963.

7

It took a long time for women to win the right to vote. Most men felt that women could not and should not vote.

Many women worked hard for the right to vote. One was Elizabeth Cady Stanton. Another was Lucretia Mott. In 1848 these two women led a meeting in Seneca Falls, New York, to discuss ways to get the vote for women.

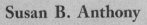

Susan B. Anthony

Susan B. Anthony was a schoolteacher who took up the cause of women's rights. For the rest of her life she worked hard for women's suffrage. She died in 1906, 14 years before women were finally given the vote. In 1979 she became the first woman pictured on a regular U.S. coin, the Susan B. Anthony dollar.

© 2007 Macmillan/McGraw-Hill

⌒ Women fighting for their right to vote were called suffragists.

The fight continued for the next 70 years. In 1878 a bill saying that women should have the right to vote was sent to **Congress**. Congress did not pass the bill. Every year for more than forty years Congress voted no. Finally, in 1919, Congress voted yes. Women had won the right to vote.

Word Workout

WORDS TO KNOW

crouch	grace	official	pitiful
sleek	sleepy	strolled	

Charades Choose a word from the list. Without telling me the word, give me some hints and clues to guess the word. After I guess, tell me the word you were thinking of. Then we'll use it in a sentence.

SPELLING WORDS

careful	cheerful	helpful	colorful
harmful	peaceful	pitiful	carefully
peacefully	painless	priceless	helpless
helplessly	sleepless	rainless	

Switcheroo I'll give you a word to spell. After you spell it, can you change the suffix and use **ful, less,** or **ly** for the ending? It won't work for all words.

(fold here)

© Macmillan/McGraw-Hill

Home-School Connection

Dear Family Member:

We're reading *Mother to Tigers* in class this week. It's a biography of Helen Martini, who set up the first nursery for baby animals in a zoo. The author tells us her story from when she first began treating baby animals at home to when the Bronx Zoo gave her a place to care for young animals. He tells us how her work led to animal nurseries all over America. I think the author wrote this story because he believed we should all help take care of animals. He used Helen Martini as an example. He also wanted us to know her story.

This Week's Skills

Comprehension: author's purpose

Vocabulary: adding **y** and **ly**

Spelling/Phonics: words with **ful, less,** and **ly**

Name _____

On Purpose

Why would you write different kinds of books and stories? Let's list one or two purposes.

MARY HAD A LITTLE LAMB...
nursery rhyme

e-mail to a friend

letter to the principal

DEAR SIR,

Principal's Office

biography

Mark Twain

The Quest for the Magic Ring
fantasy

story

The Three Little Pigs

Once Upon a Time...

Ejercicio de palabras

PALABRAS DE VOCABULARIO

crouch	grace	official	pitiful
sleek	sleepy	strolled	

Charadas Escoge una palabra de la lista. Sin decirme la palabra, dame algunos indicios y pistas para adivinar la palabra. Después que adivine, dime la palabra que estabas pensando. Luego, la usaremos en una oración.

PALABRAS DE ORTOGRAFÍA

careful	cheerful	helpful	colorful
harmful	peaceful	pitiful	carefully
peacefully	painless	priceless	helpless
helplessly	sleepless	rainless	

Cambio inesperado Te voy a dar una palabra para deletrear. Después de deletrearla, ¿puedes cambiar el sufijo y usar **ful, less** o **ly** como terminación? Esto no va a funcionar con todas las palabras.

(fold here)

© Macmillan/McGraw-Hill

Conexión con el hogar

Queridos familiares:

Estamos leyendo *Mother to Tigers* en la clase esta semana. Es una biografía de Helen Martini, una mujer que estableció una guardería para animales bebés en un zoológico. El autor nos cuenta la historia de ella desde la primera vez que comenzó a tratar a animales bebés en su casa hasta que el zoológico del Bronx le dio un lugar para cuidar a los animales bebés. Él nos cuenta cómo el trabajo de ella llevó a que se establecieran guarderías de animales por todo Estados Unidos. Pienso que el autor escribió este relato porque cree que todos debemos ayudar a cuidar a los animales. Él usó a Helen Martini como un ejemplo. Además, él también quería que conociéramos la historia de ella.

Destrezas de la semana

Comprensión: propósito del autor

Vocabulario: añadir **y** y **ly**

Ortografía/Fonética: palabras con **ful, less** y **ly**

Nombre _____

A propósito

¿Por qué escribirías diferentes tipos de libros y relatos? Vamos a decidir lo que queremos contar.

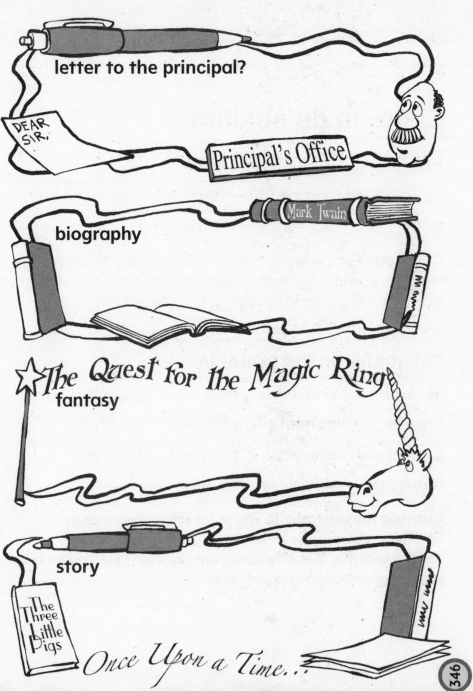

Comprehension Check

Summarize

Use an Author's Purpose Chart to tell why the author wrote about Jane Goodall. Then find details in the text to support your ideas. Use the chart to summarize the book.

Clues

↓

Author's Purpose

Think and Compare

1. Look back to pages 8–9. What words does the author use to bring David Graybeard's actions to life for the reader? *(Evaluate Author's Purpose)*

2. Think of a time when you saw an animal do something intelligent that surprised you. Describe it. *(Apply)*

3. How do you think Jane Goodall's research affects our lives today? *(Evaluate)*

Jane Goodall
Life Among the Chimpanzees

by Steven Otfinoski

Table of Contents

Chapter 1

Meet Jane Goodall

Picture some chimpanzees in the African rainforest. One young chimp rides on its mother's back. Two chimps romp and play tag. Two others sit and **groom** one another.

Sitting quietly nearby is a young woman. She waits. She watches. She jots down notes. She wants to learn as much as she can about the chimps' **behavior**. Her name is Jane Goodall.

Jane's interest in animals began when she was a child. She was eager to learn about all kinds of creatures. Once her parents found a sleepy Jane in bed with earthworms under her pillow!

⌒ Jane posed for this picture while attending a conference on the environment.

© 2007 Macmillan/McGraw-Hill

Jane Goodall: Life Among the Chimpanzees

Glossary

anthropologist *(an-thruh-POL-uh-jist)* a scientist who studies different groups of people and their customs and beliefs *(page 4)*

behavior *(bi-HAY-vyuhr)* to act in a certain way *(page 2)*

conservation *(kon-suhr-VAY-shuhn)* the careful use of something, such as a natural resource *(page 13)*

fossil *(FOS-suhl)* the remains of a plant, animal, or human hardened in rock *(page 4)*

groom *(GREWM)* clean and comb an animal's fur *(page 2)*

primate *(PRYE-mate)* a group of animals that includes human beings, monkeys, and apes *(page 7)*

reserve *(ri-ZURV)* land used for a special purpose *(page 5)*

Index

Louis Leakey chose the right person to study chimps. Jane learned so much about them. Now her time is spent sharing what she has learned with others. She hopes that people everywhere will want to protect the chimps so that they will be around forever.

"Hundreds and thousands of Roots and Shoots can solve the problems, change the world, and make it a better place to live."

—*Jane Goodall*

Jane spends a lot of her time talking about how to save the endangered chimps.

Kenya is located in the eastern part of Africa

When Jane grew up, she wanted to go to Africa to see animals in their natural home. She got her chance when a school friend invited her to visit her parents' farm in Kenya in east Africa. Jane saved money for the trip and left for Africa.

After her visit to the farm, she went to Kenya's capital, Nairobi. She wanted to stay in Africa so she went looking for a job.

At that time, a famous scientist was working in Kenya. His name was Louis Leakey. Jane went to see him and he hired her as a secretary.

Chapter 2
Gombe

Leakey was impressed with Jane's energy and love of animals. He was interested in studying the behavior of chimps in Tanzania. These chimps were living in an area far from people. He asked Jane if she would like to go there to observe and record the chimps' behaviors. She jumped at the chance. She thought the study would take three years. Instead, it took more than thirty!

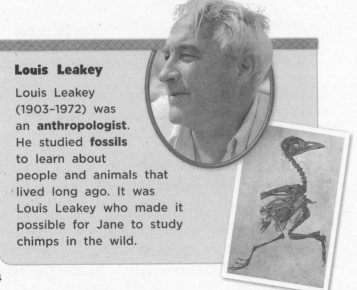

Louis Leakey

Louis Leakey (1903–1972) was an **anthropologist**. He studied **fossils** to learn about people and animals that lived long ago. It was Louis Leakey who made it possible for Jane to study chimps in the wild.

She has also helped set up homes for young, orphaned, or injured chimps in Africa. Once they are big and well enough to be on their own, they are set free in the wild.

In 1986 Jane helped found the Committee for the **Conservation** and Care of Chimpanzees. Officials of this group work to make adults and children aware of the dangers facing chimps.

Jane's life today is busier than ever. She travels to many places to give speeches about saving and helping animals.

ROOTS AND SHOOTS

Jane set up clubs for students to learn about wildlife and conservation. They are called Roots and Shoots. She started the group in Africa in 1991. Today, more than fifteen countries have Roots and Shoots groups. The groups encourage young people to take a role in protecting the environment.

Conclusion

Saving the Chimps

As the years passed, many of the chimps that Jane grew to know and love died. Other chimps were losing their habitat as people cut down the rainforests. Some chimps were captured. Some lived pitiful lives in labs where they were used in experiments.

Jane has spoken out for better treatment of captive chimps. She has called for the saving of wild chimps' homelands in books and articles.

DID YOU KNOW?

Jane Goodall has written books for children. The best-known one is called *My Life with the Chimpanzees*.

12

↑ Jane spent many years in Gombe.

Jane went to the Gombe Stream Game **Reserve** and set up camp by the side of a lake. On her first morning she set out to make contact with the chimps. When the chimps first saw her, they were scared and ran away. Jane could not get close to them. She followed them and watched them. She recorded what she saw and she waited.

5

🎧 Mother chimps and their babies stay together until the babies are at least 7 years old.

Then one day a large male chimp strolled into camp. He was after a banana that Jane had left on a table. She named him David Greybeard. After that, Jane left lots of bananas around.

The chimps were slowly getting used to Jane. They didn't run away when she came near them. They learned that she would not harm them. She would crouch and watch them all day. She took notes of everything they did.

6

Jane learned that chimps were not always peaceful. In the 1970s a new group of chimps moved into the area. Jane's chimp family went to war to drive them away. They waved tree branches and screamed at the newcomers. At times the two groups would throw rocks at each other.

Jane loved every part of her life at Gombe. The things she discovered there changed the way people think of chimpanzees. And her findings made her famous. In 1964 her picture was on the cover of a magazine, and a film was made about her and the chimps.

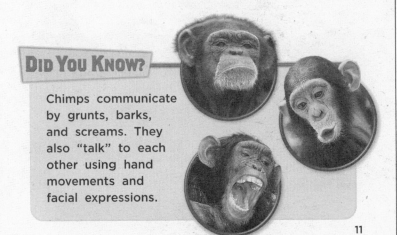

DID YOU KNOW?

Chimps communicate by grunts, barks, and screams. They also "talk" to each other using hand movements and facial expressions.

11

↺ Jane's patience helped her to gain the chimps' confidence.

10

As Jane watched the chimps, she learned more about their behaviors. They lived together in groups, and they moved as a group from place to place.

Most times the chimps were peaceful. They hugged, kissed, and held hands. They rested in the trees. They enjoyed grooming each other. One chimp would pick the ticks and dirt off the sleek body of another. Then the second chimp would groom the first.

DID YOU KNOW?

✦ Chimps are **primates**.

✦ Chimpanzees live only in the tropical rainforests, woodlands, swamps, grasslands of east and central Africa.

✦ They eat leaves, fruit, flowers, termites, ants, and small animals.

✦ They live about 60 years in captivity, but only 35 to 40 years in the wild.

7

Chapter 3
Discoveries

There were about 100 chimps in Gombe. Jane got to know many of them very well. She knew what they were like and what made them different from one another.

One day Jane saw David Greybeard pick a twig from a tree. He took off the tiny leaves and branches. He worked with careful grace. Then he stuck the twig into a termite mound. When he pulled it up again, it was covered with fat termites. The chimp ate the juicy insects.

DID YOU KNOW?

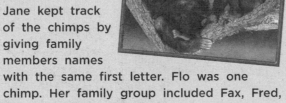

Jane kept track of the chimps by giving family members names with the same first letter. Flo was one chimp. Her family group included Fax, Fred, Flirt, and Fudge.

© 2007 Macmillan/McGraw-Hill

Jane was amazed. David had made a tool and used it. This was something it was thought only people could do.

Later Jane saw chimps take leaves and use them like a sponge to soak up water to drink. Jane reported her findings to Dr. Leakey. He was very pleased.

This chimp uses a tool to get a tasty treat.

Word Workout

WORDS TO KNOW

capture   disappear   enclosure   harming

involved   protect   supply

Crossword Fun Let's make up a crossword puzzle using the words. When we have the words in place, we can write clues. We might even give the puzzle to a member of our family or to a friend to solve.

SPELLING WORDS

about   behind   because   before   alive

attract   attend   around   kettle   tickle

hammer   rubber   puddle   people   better

Say It with Feeling I'll point to a word. Say the word, putting stress on the right syllable. We could say the words in rhythm, like a rap song: a•**bout** [pause] be•**hind** [pause] be•**cause**.

Home-School Connection

Dear Family Member:

I'm reading *Home-Grown Butterflies* in class this week. It's a real story about how people raise butterflies in Costa Rica. In this one village, there were fewer and fewer fish to eat and sell for money. Soon they would have to cut down trees from the rain forest in order to farm the land. A scientist taught the school kids how to start a butterfly farm! They now sell the pupae, or eggs, to zoos. My conclusion is that those kids are serious about protecting their environment.

This Week's Skills

Comprehension: draw conclusions

Vocabulary: words with more than one meaning

Spelling/Phonics: syllables

Name _____

Clues to a Conclusion

Let's look at the sentences. They are conclusions to parts of a story. We can decide what led up to the conclusion.

Maria and Orlando had the money they needed.

They were prepared for the rain.

Sparky, my dog, was ready for a long sleep.

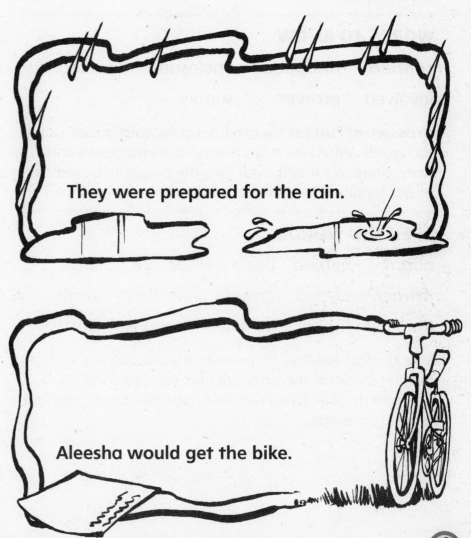

Aleesha would get the bike.

Ejercicio de palabras

PALABRAS DE VOCABULARIO

capture   disappear   enclosure   harming

involved   protect   supply

Crucigramas divertidos Armemos un crucigrama usando las palabras. Una vez que tengamos las palabras en sus lugares, podemos escribir las pistas. Incluso le podríamos dar el crucigrama a un familiar nuestro o a un amigo para resolverlo.

PALABRAS DE ORTOGRAFÍA

about   behind   because   before   alive

attract   attend   around   kettle   tickle

hammer   rubber   puddle   people   better

Dilo con ritmo Voy a señalar una palabra. Di la palabra acentuando la sílaba correcta. Podemos decir las palabras con un ritmo, como si fuera una canción de rap: a•**bout** [pausa] be•**hind** [pausa] be•**cause**.

(fold here)

© Macmillan/McGraw-Hill

Conexión con el hogar

Queridos familiares:

Estoy leyendo *Home-Grown Butterflies* en la clase esta semana. Es la historia real de cómo la gente cría mariposas en Costa Rica. En este pueblo en especial, cada vez había menos y menos peces para comer y para. Al poco tiempo, tendrían que comenzar a talar los árboles del bosque tropical para poder sembrar la tierra. ¡Un científico les enseñó a los niños de una escuela cómo comenzar una granja de mariposas! Ahora ellos venden las pupas, o los huevos, a los zoológicos. Mi conclusión es que esos niños son bien serios cuando se trata de proteger su medio ambiente.

Destrezas de la semana

Comprensión: sacar conclusiones

Vocabulario: palabras con más de un significado

Ortografía/Fonética: sílabas

Nombre _____

Pistas para una conclusión

Miremos las oraciones. Son las conclusiones de las partes de un relato. Podemos decidir qué fue lo que llevó a cada conclusión.

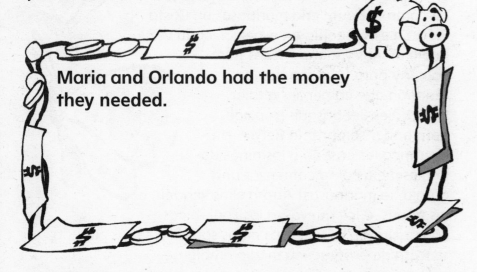

Maria and Orlando had the money they needed.

Sparky, my dog, was ready for a long sleep.

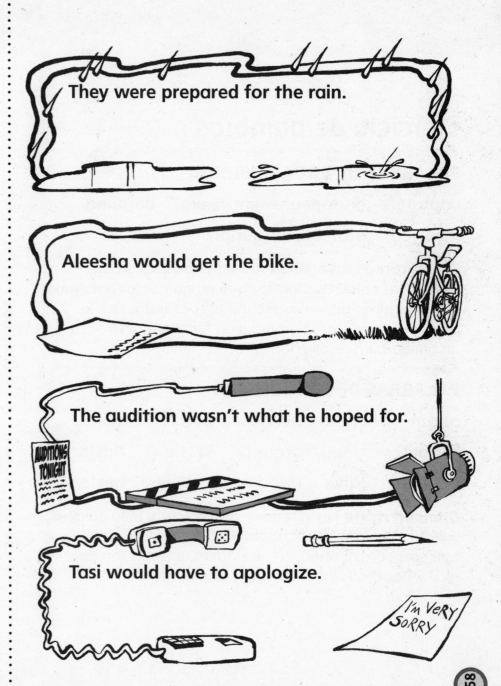

They were prepared for the rain.

Aleesha would get the bike.

The audition wasn't what he hoped for.

Tasi would have to apologize.

358

Comprehension Check

Summarize

Use a Draw Conclusions Chart to tell about loosestrife. Do you think people should be concerned about loosestrife? Why?

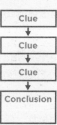

Think and Compare

1. Turn to pages 12–13 in this book. What do you think the students learned by helping solve the loosestrife problem? *(Draw Conclusions)*

2. If you visited a wetlands area, what would you do to make sure you didn't carry seeds home with you? Why? *(Apply)*

3. Non-native plants are still coming into this country. Some stores sell them to people who plant them in their gardens. What do you think might happen as a result of this? *(Evaluate)*

Purple Loosestrife
The Beautiful Invader

by Doris Licameli

Table of Contents

Introduction

Wetlands are beautiful places. They are watery lowland areas that bustle with life. Marshes, swamps, and bogs are kinds of wetlands. Pond edges and the banks of streams and rivers are, too. **Native** plants, grasses, and trees bloom near the water. They provide food and shelter for many kinds of wildlife.

Ravens make their nests in the trees. Turtles bask on the rocks. You may even see a fox or a raccoon washing food in the water. But the bustling **environment** is in danger if purple loosestrife shows up.

⋒ This is what a thriving wetland looks like.

Glossary

ecosystem *(EE-koh-sis-tuhm)* a community of living things *(page 6)*

environment *(en-VIGH-ruhn-muhnt)* the place or condition where plants, animals, and humans live *(page 2)*

herb *(UHRB)* a plant used in medicine or as a seasoning *(page 4)*

native *(NAY-tiv)* a plant or animal that lives or grows in a particular place *(page 2)*

natural *(NACH-uhr-uhl)* something real or alive, acting in the usual way *(page 6)*

nature *(NAY-chuhr)* everything that is living *(page 3)*

rootstock *(ROOT-stahk)* a root that a plant uses to reproduce *(page 9)*

weevil *(WEE-vil)* one of many small beetles whose larvae can destroy plants *(page 6)*

Index

Conclusion

Immigrants may have brought purple loosestrife here for their new gardens. No one knew it could be so harmful. In time, it became a beautiful invader with nothing to stop it from spreading. Now there are beetles to attack the marsh monster. Our native plants are sprouting again. Can the return of frogs, birds, and fish be far behind?

⟳ This wetland is free of loosestrife and is thriving.

When loosestrife starts growing, it harms native plants. They get choked off and die. With food and shelter gone, the wildlife disappears. The balance of **nature** is upset. It's no wonder loosestrife is called a marsh monster.

⟳ Marshes are in many places in North America.

Wetlands areas

⟳ Purple loosestrife has spread to almost every state in our country. It has also invaded parts of Canada.

Chapter 1
Where Did the Marsh Monster Come From?

Purple loosestrife has been around a long time. It is a native plant in Europe and Asia. The plant did not become a pest in those places. It didn't grow out of control as it has here. In fact, some people thought it was a helpful **herb**. They used it as a medicine. How did it get from there to here?

Purple loosestrife came to North America in the 1800s, but no one is sure how it traveled. Could seeds have been carried across the sea in ships?

The Language of Flowers

Hanakotoba (HAN•uh•koh•toh•buh) is the "language of flowers" in Japan. It tells the meaning of each flower. According to Hanakotoba, purple loosestrife is a flower that tells of sadness.

Beetles Can Help

The students started out with 100 beetles the first year. That meant that after eight weeks they had 10,000 beetles to release. Some science classes saved 300 of the beetles for the next round.

The students brought back loosestrife rootstocks from a nearby wetland. They planted them in pots in the pool. Water covered the bottom of the pool. The plants grew fast. When they reached 24 inches tall, it was time to add the beetles.

A screen was put around each plant so that the beetles couldn't get out. The students placed ten beetles on each plant. They soon learned that one beetle could hatch over 100 offspring! The life cycle of these beetles is eight weeks. After a while they placed the beetles in the wetland where the marsh monster was choking other plants.

© 2007 Macmillan/McGraw-Hill

Chapter 5

How Can We Get Involved?

Millions more beetles were needed. Scientists asked some schools for help. They thought raising beetles would make a great science project.

Students at Highland High School in Indiana were eager to become involved. Students from schools in Markesan, Wisconsin joined the project too.

They began with a supply of beetles and an ordinary plastic wading pool. The pool served as an enclosure where the purple loosestrife plants would grow.

↻ The students used ordinary things to grow the plants.

↻ Early immigrants sailed in ships like these across the seas.

Many people believe a supply of seeds arrived in the baggage of new immigrants. They planted the seeds in their new gardens. The purple flowers may have reminded them of home.

Did you Know?

Almost 100 percent of purple loosestrife seeds that are planted will sprout and grow.

Chapter 2
Why Did the Marsh Monster Spread?

Purple loosestrife did not grow out of control in Europe and Asia. It did not kill its plant neighbors. Why? The answer is simple. Purple loosestrife had **natural** enemies in its homeland. Certain beetles fed on the roots, leaves, and stems. They kept the plant in check. They were all involved in the same **ecosystem**.

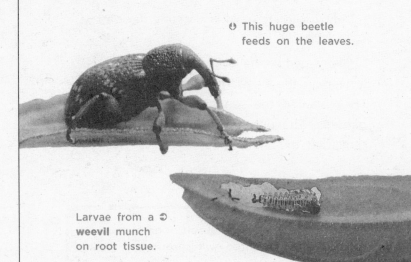

↻ This huge beetle feeds on the leaves.

Larvae from a ↻ **weevil** munch on root tissue.

This site shows the ↻ land before the beetles were released.

↻ This photo shows the same site after the beetles were there.

© 2007 Macmillan/McGraw-Hill

Many scientists started to research. They hoped to find beetles and weevils that would eat only purple loosestrife.

They didn't want bugs that might destroy other plants by mistake. They chose four insects to study more closely.

After going to Europe to capture a supply, they raised the beetles here at home. At last the time came when they could release the beetles. At some test sites, the beetles ate almost all of the purple loosestrife.

Chapter 4
Where Can Help Be Found?

People have used chemical sprays to kill patches of loosestrife. But it grew right back again. Burning and flooding the loosestrife did not help either.

In order to protect wetlands from further harm, scientists had to think hard. They needed to find a better way to fight the pest. They came up with a plan. They would learn more about the marsh monster's natural enemies—beetles. Maybe the scientists could capture beetles and bring them here. But would it be safe to set them loose in North America?

Did you Know?

Birds called black terns were once a common breeding species in northern New York. They disappeared at the same time purple loosestrife invaded the area.

Giant Reed

Another wetland invader is the giant reed. It was brought to California in the 1700s. It is a huge plant that looks like bamboo. These reeds grow four to five inches a day, and many reach 25 feet (7.6 m) high. Now giant reeds cover thousands of acres. Like purple loosestrife, they choke off native plants.

When purple loosestrife got to North America, its natural enemies stayed behind. The beetles that might have kept it from growing so much were not here. It began to grow taller than before, and its root systems grew stronger and longer. Native wetland seeds were crowded out. These plants began to die out.

Cattails are being crowded ↻ out by purple loosestrife.

Did you Know?

Some marsh monsters grow up to 25 feet (7.6 m) tall.

Chapter 3
How Did the Seeds Travel?

Each loosestrife plant can produce almost three million seeds a year. The seeds are tiny and light. They can travel far on a gust of wind.

Sometimes seeds take a ride on an animal's fur. Even a field mouse can carry seeds on its back. A human visitor to a wetland site should be careful, too. Purple loosestrife seeds might cling to pants or travel in a pair of boots.

↺ Purple loosestrife seeds can hitchhike on almost anything.

Purple loosestrife seeds sprout quickly. **Rootstocks** grow about one foot a year. A rootstock is like an underground stem that grows sideways. Plants shoot up from the rootstock. They can flower in their first growing season. A mature plant can grow many spikes from a single "stem." Some send up between 30 and 50 spikes each spring. In time, they can make a sea of purple flowers

This diagram shows how spikes ↻ grow from a rootstock.

Did you Know?

The marsh monster's rootstocks are so strong, they can even grow in gravel, sand, clay, or between rocks.

Calendar

_____

Monday	Tuesday	Wednesday	Thursday	Friday

Name _____

Calendar

_____

Monday	Tuesday	Wednesday	Thursday	Friday

Name _____

Calendar

_____

Monday	Tuesday	Wednesday	Thursday	Friday

Name _____

Calendar

_____

Monday	Tuesday	Wednesday	Thursday	Friday

Name _____

Calendar

_____

Monday	Tuesday	Wednesday	Thursday	Friday

Name _____

Calendar

_____

Monday	Tuesday	Wednesday	Thursday	Friday

Name _____

Calendar

Monday	Tuesday	Wednesday	Thursday	Friday

Name _____

Calendar

Monday	Tuesday	Wednesday	Thursday	Friday

Name _____

Calendar

_____

Monday	Tuesday	Wednesday	Thursday	Friday

Name _____

Calendar

_____

Monday	Tuesday	Wednesday	Thursday	Friday

Name _____

Credits

Unit 1 Week 3 *On Level Saving the Rainforest*
2–3: (bkgd) ©DigitalVision/Punchstock. 3: (c) ©Bruce Coleman Inc/ Alamy; (br) ©Eric Horan/AGEfotostock. 4: ©T. Loman/AGEfotostock. 6: ©Tropicalstock.net/Ala my. 7: (b) ©Bjorn Svensson/AGEfotostock; (br) ©Enigma/Alamy. 8: (t) ©Ray Coleman/Visuals Unlimited; (t) ©Tono Labra/ AGEfotostock. 9: (b) ©T H Foto/Alamy. (t) ©Angelo Cavalli/Superstock. 10: (c) ©John Kaprielin/PhotoResearchers; (b) National Tropical Botanical Garden. 11: (b) ©Wayne Lawler/CORBIS. 12: ©David Dudenhoefer/Odyssey Productions, Chicago. 13: ©Randall Hyman. 14: (br) ©C Squared Studios/Getty Images; (bc) ©C Squared Studios/Getty Images; (bkgd) ©Digital Vision/Punchstock. TOC: C Squared Studios/Getty Images.

Unit 1 Week 4 *On Level The Weddell Seals of Antarctica*
3: (b) ©John Digby/Alamy. (t) ©Michele Burgess/Superstock. 4: ©Rick Price/CORBIS. 6: ©SD Photo/CORBIS. 8: ©Norbert Wu/Peter Arnold Inc. 9: ©Norbert Wu/Peter Arnold Inc.; (cr) ©Picture Library Johnson/CORBIS; (cl) ©Stephen Frink/CORBIS. (br) ©Rick Price/CORBIS. 12: ©Rick Price/CORBIS. 13: ©Galen Waldhaus/Alamy. 14: ©Wolfgang Koehler/CORBIS. CVR: ©Bruce Rowell/CORBIS. TOC: ©Rick Price/CORBIS.

Unit 2 Week 3 *On Level Incredible Inventions: Computers*
2: (br) ©Ryan McVay/Getty Images; (bl) ©William Whitehurst/CORBIS. 2–3: (bkgd) PhotoDisc/Getty Images. 3: (t) ©Gary Buss/Getty Images; (b) ©Photodisc/Getty Images. 4: (b) Photodisc/ Getty Images. 6: (c) ©Bettmann/CORBIS. 6–7: (bkgd) ©Ryan McVay/Getty Images. 6: (t) ©Photodisc/Getty Images. 7: (tr) ©StockTrek/Getty Images. 8: ©StockTrek/ Getty Images. 9: (t) ©CORBIS; (bkgd) ©StockTrek/Getty Images. 10: (tr) ©Epictura/Alamy. (c) ©Jose Luis Pelaez, Inc./CORBIS. 8–9: (bkgd) (cr) ©Epictura/Alamy; (c) ©Jose Luis Pelaez, Inc./CORBIS. 10: (b) ©IBM. 8: ©PhotoDisc/Getty Images. 9: (b) ©PhotoDisc/Getty Images. 11: ©Bill Aron/ PhotoEdit. 10–11: (t) (bkgd) ©PhotoDisc/Getty Images. 12: (t) ©Michael Newman/PhotoEdit. 12: (t) AP/Wide World Photos. 12–13: (bkgd) ©NASA/ handout/Reuters/CORBIS; (bkgd) ©Photodisc/Getty Images. 14: (t) (b) ©NASA/ ©William Whitehurst/CORBIS. (bkgd) ©PhotoDisc/Getty Images. CVR: (c) ©Gary Buss/Getty Images.

Unit 2 Week 4 *On Level The International Space Station*
2–3: ©NASA. (bkgd) ©StockTrek/Getty Images. 4: ©StockTrek/Getty Images. 5: (tr) ©NASA. (bkgd) ©StockTrek/Getty Images. 6: (c) ©NASA; Images. 5: (tr) ©Photodisc/Getty Images. 6–7: (bc) ©NASA. 7: (tr) ©Roger Russmeyer/CORBIS. (bkgd) ©StockTrek/Getty Images. 8: ©StockTrek/ Getty Images. 9: (t) ©CORBIS; (bkgd) ©StockTrek/Getty Images. 10: (tr) ©NASA; (bkgd) ©StockTrek/Getty Images. 11: (t) ©NASA; (bkgd) ©StockTrek/Getty Images. 13: (cr) ©CORBIS; (bkgd) ©StockTrek/Getty Images. 12: (b) ©NASA; (bkgd) ©PhotoDisc/Getty Images. 14: (b) ©StockTrek/Getty Images; (tr) ©StockTrek/Getty Images. CVR: (bkgd) ©NASA/CORBIS; (tc) ©StockTrek/Getty Images; (tr) ©StockTrek/Getty Images. TOC: (c) ©CORBIS. (l) ©StockTrek/Getty Images.

Unit 2 Week 5 *On Level E.B. White, Writer*
2: (tl) ©Bettmann/CORBIS 4: (b) "By permission of the E.B. White Estate." E.B. White Collection, Cornell University Library; 1899–1985. Courtesy of the Division of Rare and Manuscript Collections, Cornell University Library. 6: "By permission of the "E.B. White Estate" E.B. White Collection, Hill. 6: "By permission of the "E.B. White Estate" E.B. White Collection, 1899–1985. Courtesy of the Division of Rare and Manuscript Collections, Cornell University Library. 7: (tr) ©E.A. Jones/AGEfotostock; (cl) Jules Frazier/Getty Images; (tr) ©Macmillan/McGraw-Hill. 8: (b) ©Lake County Museum/CORBIS. 9: (t) "By permission of the E.B. White Estate" E.B. White Collection, 1899–1985. Courtesy of the Division of Rare and Manuscript Collections, Cornell University Library. 10: (tl) Macmillan/ McGraw-Hill. 11: (tr) ©Michael Greenlar/The Image Works. 12: (cr) ©Reuters/CORBIS. 13: (b) Jeff Vanuga/CORBIS. 14: (b) ©Bettmann/ CORBIS. 3: Cover permission for The TRUMPET OF THE SWAN by E.B. White: illustrated by Fred Marcellino. Reprinted by permission of the HarperCollins Publishers. 3: Cover permission for CHARLOTTE'S WEB by E.B. White, illustrated by Garth Williams. Illustrations copyright renewed © 1980 by Estate of Garth Williams. Reprinted by permission of HarperCollins Publishers. 3: Cover permission for STUART LITTLE by E. B. White; illustrated y Garth Williams. Illustrations copyright renewed © 1973 by estate of Garth Williams. Reprinted by permission of HarperCollins Publishers.

Unit 3 Week 3 *On Level Water in the Desert*
2: (br) ©Buff&Gerald Corsi/Visuals Unlimited. 2–3: (bkgd) ©Bruce Heinemann/Getty Images. 3: (t) ©DigitalVision/AGE Fotostock. 4: ©George H.H. Huey/CORBIS. 5: (t) ©George H.H. Huey/CORBIS; (bkgd) ©Bruce Heinemann/Getty Images. 6: (r) ©WorldWide Picture Library/Alamy; (bkgd) ©Gregory G. Dimijian M.D./ PhotoResearchers; (tr) ©Walt Anderson/Visuals Unlimited. 7: (br) ©Gregory G. Dimijian M.D./ ©George

Unit 3 Week 3 *On Level Thrills and Chills*
2–3: ©Tommaso di Girolamo/AGEfotostock. 4: ©Stapleton Collection/ Corbis. 5: (t) ©Historical Picture Archive/CORBIS. 5: (inset) ©Christie's Images/Superstock; (bc) C Squared/Getty Images. 7: Reproduced from the Collections of the Library of Congress. 9: (b) ©Haruyoshi Yamaguchi/ CORBIS; (tr) ©Mark Segal/IndexStock. 11: ©Bettmann/CORBIS. 13: (b) IndexStock. TOC: ©Bernd Mellman/Alamy.

Unit 5 Week 2 *On Level John Muir: Friend of Nature*
2: (br) ©BrandX Pictures. 2–3: (bkgd) ©Gerald French/CORBIS. 3: (inset) ©Galen Rowell/CORBIS. 4: (b) ©TK; (t) ©Siede Preis/Getty Images. 5: ©Bettmann/CORBIS. 6: (bl) ©Siede Preis/Getty Images. 6–7: (c) ©Tom Bean/CORBIS. 7: (tl) ©Siede Preis/Getty Images. 8: (br) ©Gavin Hellier/ Alamy. (tl) ©Robert Glusic/AGEfotostock. 10: (b) ©Robert Mackinlay/Peter Arnold. 11: (t) ©Royalty-FreeCORBIS; (inset) ©Bettmann/CORBIS; (t) ©Siede Preis/Getty Images. 11: (t) ©Royalty-FreeCORBIS; (inset) ©Adam Jones/PhotoResearchers. 12–13: (t) © Robert Glusic/AGEfotostock. 14: ©Galen Rowell/CORBIS. CVR: (cr) ©BrandX Pictures; (bkgd) ©Gerald French/CORBIS. TOC: ©TK; ©C Squared Studios/Getty Images

Unit 5 Week 1 *On Level Children at Work: On the Frontier*
photo credits: 2: ©CORBIS. 3: ©Photo Collection Alexander Alland, Sr. /CORBIS. 5: 'Baltimore Album' Quilt, c. 1840s (cotton), American School, (19th century)/©Museum of Fine Arts, Houston, Texas, USA, Gift of Mrs. John D. Rockefeller/Bridgeman Art Library. 6: (tl) ©CORBIS; (br) ©Thad Samuels Abell Lil/Getty Images. 7: ©Bettmann/CORBIS. 8: Hulton Archive/Getty Images. 9: (tr) ©HistoricGraphics.com/Kelbaugh Collection; (tl) ©HistoricGraphics.com/Kelbaugh Collection. (t) Macmillan/McGraw-Hill. 10: ©CORBIS. 11: ©Bettmann/CORBIS. 12: ©Bettmann/CORBIS. COV: (r) ©HistoricGraphics.com/ ©CORBIS. 14: ©Bettmann/CORBIS. COV: (c) ©CORBIS. TOC: (tc) ©Bettmann/ CORBIS.

Unit 4 Week 4 *On Level Patching a Playground*
2–3: (bc) Courtesy the Hickey Family. 3: (cr) Courtesy the Hickey family. 5: Courtesy the Hickey family. 6: (tl) Courtesy the Hickey family; (br) Courtesy the Hickey family. 8: Courtesy the Hickey family. 9: (tl) Courtesy the Hickey family. 10: Courtesy the Hickey family. 11: Courtesy the Hickey family. 12: Courtesy the Hickey family. 13: Courtesy the Hickey family. COV: (bl) Courtesy the Hickey family. 14: Courtesy the Hickey family; (br) Courtesy the Hickey family. TOC: Courtesy the Hickey family.

Unit 4 Week 1 *On Level Enjoying our Natural Resources*
2–3: (bc) ©RoyaltyFree/CORBIS. 4: (bkgd) ©Walter Bibikow/IndexStock. (tl) ©DigitalVision/ Punchstock. 5: (tl) S.Wanke/PhotoLink/Getty Images; (b) ©Will Elwell/Superstock. 7: Karl Weatherly/Getty Images. 6: ©Pixtal/Superstock. 7: (cr) Fred Lyons/Cole Group/Getty Images. 8: (b) ©Geoffrey Morgan/Alamy. (tl) Robert Glusic/Getty Images. 9: ©PhotoDisc/Getty Images. 10: ©RoyaltyFree/ CORBIS. 11: (c) ©RoyaltyFree/CORBIS. (tl) PhotoLink/ Getty Images; (bkgd) PhotoLink/Getty Images. 12: (tl) ©Zefa/Masterfile; (tr) ©Dale Wilson/Masterfile. 13: ©Pixtal/AGEfotostock. 14: ©SteveSkjold/Alamy. CVR: ©Pixtal/Superstock. TOC: ©Royalty Free/ CORBIS.

Unit 4 Week 1 *On Level Oops! Food Surprises*
2–3: (bkgd) ©Don Lamont/CORBIS. 4: (br) ©Imageshop/Alamy; (bl) ©Imageshop/Alamy; (bc) ©Photick/Alamy. 5: (tr) ©Bettmann/CORBIS; (b) ©Larry Dale Gordon/Getty Images. 6: ©Roy Oons/Masterfile. 7: (tr) ©Janice Christie/Getty Images. 7: (tr) (br) ©Gianni Dagli Orti/CORBIS; (tr) PhotoLink/Getty Images. 9: (br) ©Gianni Dagli Orti/CORBIS; (tr) PhotoLink/Getty Images. 11: (tr) PhotoLink/Getty Images. 13: (tr) PhotoLink/Getty Images. 14: (tr) PhotoLink/ Getty Images. CVR: ©Toni/PhotoLink/Getty Images. TOC: ©Bob Doennmrich/PhotoEdit.

Unit 3 Week 5 *On Level Drawing Faces*
3: ©Toni/photoLink/Getty Images; ©PhotoLink/Getty Images; (tr) PhotoLink/Getty Images. 4: (br) CSquared Studios/Getty Images. 5: (tr) PhotoLink/Getty Images. 6: (br) ©Robert Harding Picture Library/Alamy. 7: (tr) PhotoLink/Getty Images. 9: (br) ©Gianni Dagli Orti/CORBIS; (tr) PhotoLink/Getty Images. 13: (tr) PhotoLink/Getty Images. 14: (tr) PhotoLink/Getty Images. CVR: ©Toni/PhotoLink/Getty Images. TOC: ©PhotoLink/Getty Images.

H.H. Huey; (br) ©John Cancalosi/AGE Fotostock. 10–11: (cr) ©Zefa/ Masterfile; (tl) ©BIOS/Peter Arnold. (b) ©Adam Jones/Visuals Unlimited; (bkgd) ©Robert Glusic/Getty Images. 12: ©Robert Cameron/Getty Images. 13: ©Robert Glusic/Getty Images. 14: (bc) ©John Burcham/Getty Images; (c) ©Bruce Heinemann/Getty Images. CVR: ©Digital Vision/ AGEfotostock. TOC: ©Digital Vision/AGEfotostock

Unit 5 Week 4 *On Level Hurricane Heroes*
2–3: ©Royalty Free/CORBIS. 6: ©Getty Images. 7: ©Jim McDonald/ CORBIS. 8: © CHARLES W LUZIER/Reuters/ Corbis. 9: ©R. Steward/Newsobserver/CORBIS/Sygma. 10: ©Getty Images. 11: ©Getty Images. 12: ©Steve Starr/ CORBIS. 13: (1) ©AFP/NOAA/Getty Images; (2) ©Naval Atlantic Meteorology and Oceanography Center/ CORBIS; (3) ©NOAA/Zuma/CORBIS; (4) ©NOAA/Zuma/ CORBIS. 14: (b) ©Roger Ball/CORBIS; (inset) ©FEMA/ Getty Images; (bl) ©James Neilson/ AFP/Getty Images. CVR: ©Joe Raedle/Getty Images. TOC: ©CORBIS.

Unit 5 Week 5 *On Level Amazing Bird Builders*
2: ©Morales/AGEfotostock. 3: (bkgd) ©Jeremy Woodhouse/Masterfile; (bl) ©Jane Sapinsky/Superstock. 4: ©Dinodia/AGEfotostock. 5: ©Pat Bennet/ Alamy. 6: ©Joe MacDonald/CORBIS. 7: ©Macmillan/McGraw-Hill. 8: ©Frank Lane Picture Agency/CORBIS. 9: ©David Ellis/Visuals Unlimited. 10–11: (bkgd) ©Michael&Patricia Fogden/CORBIS. 12: ©Carol Buchanan/ Alamy. 13: (bkgd) ©DNStock/ Visuals Unlimited; (c) Macmillan/McGraw-Hill. 14: ©Edmond Van Hoorick/getty Images. CVR: (bkgd) ©Pat Bennet/Alamy; (c) Macmillan/McGraw-Hill. TOC: ©Jeremy Woodhouse/Masterfile.

Unit 6 Week 3 *On Level Getting out the Vote*
2: ©Bob Daemmrich/ Photo Edit. 3: ©Bob Daemmrich/ Photo Edit. 4: ©Bettmann/ CORBIS. 7: ©Bettmann/CORBIS. 8: (inset) ©Bettmann/ Corbis; (cr) ©CORBIS. 9: ©Bettmann/CORBIS. 10: ©Bettmann/CORBIS.

13: ©Tony Freeman/Photo Edit. 14: ©Comstock Images/Alamy. CVR: ©Comstock/ Images/Alamy. TOC: ©Bettmann/CORBIS.

Unit 6 Week 4 *On Level Jane Goodall: Life Among the Chimpanzees*
2: ©Getty Images. 4: (br) ©Kevin Schafer/Peter Arnold Inc.; (inset) ©Jonathan Blair/CORBIS. 5: ©Kennan Ward/CORBIS. 6: ©BIOS/Peter Arnold Inc. 7: ©BIOS/Peter Arnold Inc. 8: ©Tim Davis/Photo Researchers Inc. 9: ©Adam Jones/PhotoResearchers Inc. 10: ©Bruce Coleman Inc./ Alamy. 11: (1) ©Joe McDonald/CORBIS; (2) ©Tom Brakefield/CORBIS; (cr) ©DigitalVision/PunchStock. 12–13: (b) ©Bios/Peter Arnold Inc. 14: ©Getty Images. CVR–TOC: (bkgd) ©DigitalVision/PunchStock. CVR: (c) ©BIOS/ Peter Arnold Inc. TOC: (tc) ©Tim Davis/Photo researcher Inc.

Unit 6 Week 5 *On Level Purple Loosestrife:The Beautiful Invader*
2: ©Kelly Mooney/CORBIS. 3: ©Pat Anderson/Visuals Unlimited. 4: ©Pat Anderson/ Visuals Unlimited. 5: ©Fine Art Photographic Library, London / Art Resource, NY. 6: (cl) ©John T. Fowler/ Alamy; (br) ©Bernd Blossey/ Cornell. 7: ©Michael P. Gadomski/PhotoResearchers Inc. 8: ©Dave Schiefelbein/Getty Images. 10: ©William Leaman/ Alamy Images. 11: (cr) ©Doug Landis/Forestry Images; (bc) ©Doug Landis/Forestry Images. 12: ©Eric Combs/ Forestry Images. 13: Macmillan/McGraw-Hill. 14: ©H. Stanley Johnson/Superstock. CVR: ©Pat Anderson/ Visuals Unlimited. TOC: (bkgd) ©Pat Anderson/Visuals Unlimited. TOC: (inset) Macmillan/ Mcgraw Hill.